THE CANCER CRISIS IN APPALACHIA

Kentucky Students Take ACTION

2nd EDITION

EDITED BY NATHAN L. VANDERFORD & CHRIS PRICHARD

Research reported in this publication was supported by the National Cancer Institute of the National Institutes of Health under Award Number R25CA221765. The content is solely the responsibility of the authors and does not necessarily represent the official views of the National Institutes of Health.

Book design by Eric Butler

Cover photo of Red River Gorge by Alexey Stiop / Adobe Stock

ISBN 978-1-953058-46-1

Published by
Butler Books
www.butlerbooks.com

CONTENTS

HIGH SCHOOL STUDENT ESSAYS

Contents

Contents

UNDERGRADUATE STUDENT ESSAYS

PREFACE

Welcome to the second edition of *The Cancer Crisis in Appalachia: Kentucky Students Take ACTION*. This book contains essays written by a group of 19 high school and 14 undergraduate students who are Appalachian Kentucky residents and participants in the University of Kentucky Markey Cancer Center's Appalachian Career Training in Oncology (ACTION) Program. ACTION aims to prepare and motivate students to pursue oncology careers and to enhance Appalachian Kentucky community members' understanding of cancer. Ultimately, we want to use ACTION as a means of addressing the cancer disparities in the Appalachian Kentucky region.

The burden of cancer in the United States is significant: as the second leading cause of death, over 1.8 million new cancer cases and 608,000 cancer deaths are expected in 2021 [1, 2]. Kentucky bears a disproportionate cancer burden compared to other states. In fact, Kentucky ranks first in the nation in overall cancer incidence and mortality rates; no other state has higher cancer rates than does Kentucky [2]. Over 30,000 new cancer cases and 10,000 cancer deaths are expected in Kentucky in 2021 [3]. What's worse is that cancer rates are highest, by a significant amount, in the Appalachian region of Kentucky. For example, the Appalachian Kentucky lung cancer death rate is almost double the national rate [4]. This cancer burden is driven by high tobacco use, poor diets and high obesity rates, poverty, low education attainment, low medical literacy, and lack of access to and low engagement with the healthcare system [4-9]. All these factors and others brew the perfect storm that contributes to the high cancer rates in Appalachian Kentucky.

Cancer statistics paint a dim picture, but they do not capture the true personal toll of the disease. Cancer causes a range of deeply personal consequences to those with the disease as well as to their family, friends, and often, even their entire community. This is especially true for close-knit families and communities in places like Appalachian Kentucky. For those of us who have dealt with cancer, we know that the disease rips at health, emotions, and family structures.

Just like the first edition of this book, stories of cancer's personal impact, impressions of the causes of the disease and visions of what could be done to decrease cancer's prevalence are covered in this edition. I specifically have the authors describe their personal experience with cancer, discuss why they think cancer impacts their families and communities so harshly, and cover what they think can be done to lower cancer rates in Appalachia.

I have students write these essays so they can learn more about cancer and its impact. Through their writing and research, they learn about cancer epidemiology, cancer risk factors, modifiable behaviors that can lower cancer risk, and the biology of cancer. They also explore their thoughts and feelings about the disease in personal ways. As you read the essays, I think you will see that students learn a great deal about cancer and they have a lot to say about its causes and consequences and how we can tackle lowering cancer rates in Appalachia.

The essays are authentically poignant. They are told in the voice of the writer, meaning that they are sometimes raw and imperfectly polished. The students worked hard through the editing process to improve the quality of their writing and the clarity of their story while maintaining their writing style and voice. This is, in my view, a critically important part of having students write their cancer stories. Additionally, it is important that students express their personal feelings and opinions about the causes of cancer in their families and communities while balancing those feelings and opinions with evidence-based research. In some cases, these opinions and feelings may push the boundaries of what is evidence-based. However, exploring the differences between opinion and evidence is an important aspect of understanding how people in Appalachian Kentucky understand cancer and what we as cancer educators and researchers need to do to help improve cancer education and awareness in the region.

Readers will gain insight into how cancer touches youth in Appalachian Kentucky. In her essay, "Pickpocketing Our Lives: The Great Thief of Kentucky," Chezney Boothe describes cancer as "a thief, pilfering through our lives and ripping away things that cannot be replaced." In "Memories Never Made" by Zane Whitaker, you will read how cancer prevented him from making memories with his grandfather. In "Cancer: A Personal Story" by Makinna Caudill, you will learn about how her mother's battle with colon cancer shook her family and changed it forever. Each of the essays tells a unique and personal story.

I believe you will be touched as you read these essays. I hope the stories and points that the students make will lead you to think about cancer risk factors and modifiable behaviors. I hope you will be inspired to take better care of yourself and to encourage your family and friends to take better care of themselves. I hope that you will be inspired to tell others what you learned about cancer prevention and control strategies. I hope you will learn about structural and policy-level issues that contribute to Kentucky's cancer problem and how these issues need to be addressed to make significant impacts on lowering Kentucky's cancer burden. I hope you will be empowered to tell others about how bad the cancer problem is in Kentucky and that multiple steps need to be taken to change our situation. Through this, I hope we can make an impact on reducing the cancer burden in Kentucky in the long run. I also hope that you are encouraged by how bright these students are and the promise they hold for the future of Kentucky and beyond. We will all reap the benefits of the great things these students will do with their lives. I believe these students can and will help us address Kentucky's cancer burden.

Enjoy this collection of essays. Learn and be inspired to act on improving your health and the health of your family, friends, and community. Consider the structural and policy issues that could be addressed to improve health and socioeconomic conditions in Appalachian Kentucky. Take ACTION to help us reduce the cancer disparities in our beautiful Commonwealth!

—Nathan L. Vanderford, PhD, MBA
Director, Appalachian Career Training in Oncology
(ACTION) Program

REFERENCES

1. "Leading Causes of Death," Centers for Disease Control and Prevention, accessed June 14, 2021, https://www.cdc.gov/nchs/fastats/leading-causes-of-death.htm.

2. R. L. Siegel et al., "Cancer Statistics, 2021," *CA: A Cancer Journal for Clinicians* 71, no. 1 (January–February 2021): 7–33, https://acsjournals.onlinelibrary.wiley.com/doi/10.3322/caac.21654.

3. "Cancer Statistics Center: Kentucky at a Glance," American Cancer

Society, accessed 2021, https://cancerstatisticscenter.cancer.org/#!/state/Kentucky.

4. S. D. Rodriguez et al., "A Social-Ecological Review of Cancer Disparities in Kentucky," *Southern Medical Journal* 111, no. 4 (April 2018): 213–219, https://www.ncbi.nlm.nih.gov/pmc/articles/PMC5935122/.

5. M. Charlton et al., "Challenges of Rural Cancer Care in the United States," *Oncology (Williston Park)* 29, no. 9 (September 2015): 633–640, https://www.cancernetwork.com/view/challenges-rural-cancer-care-united-states.

6. "Health Disparities in Appalachia," Appalachian Regional Commission, last modified August 23, 2017, https://www.arc.gov/report/health-disparities-in-appalachia/.

7. R. A. Crosby et al., *Rural Populations and Health: Determinants, Disparities, and Solutions* (Hoboken, NJ: Wiley, 2012).

8. A. M. Lopez et al., "Epidemiology and Implementation of Cancer Prevention in Disparate Populations and Settings," *American Society of Clinical Oncology Educational Book* 39 (May 2019): 50–60, https://ascopubs.org/doi/full/10.1200/EDBK_238965.

9. S. Zuppello, "The Cancer Capital of America," *The Outline*, May 22, 2019, https://theoutline.com/post/7457/the-cancer-capital-of-america?zd=1&zi=qvjmrf2u.

HIGH SCHOOL STUDENT ESSAYS

A PROMISE FOR TOMORROW

Ceana Bays

"It's really going to happen. I really won't ever go back to school. Not ever. I'll never be famous or leave anything worthwhile behind. I'll never go to college or have a job. I won't see my brother grow up. I won't travel, never earn money, never drive, never fall in love or leave home or get my own house.

It's really, really true.

A thought stabs up, growing from my toes and ripping through me, until it stifles everything else and becomes the only thing I'm thinking. It fills me up like a silent scream."

—Jenny Downham, *Before I Die*

My name is Ceana Bays, and this year I am a freshman at George Rogers Clark High School. I was born and raised in Kentucky, and I am 14 years old. In school, I am in a women's choir and I focus on my grades and maintaining my 4.0 GPA. Outside of school, I spend my time volunteering with my youth group. Helping the community has always given me a feeling of fulfillment. Spending time with my family, friends, and animals has always been very important to me. Through the past few years, I've really thought about what kind of career I would like to focus on, and for me, it has always been in the medical field. It is a dream of mine to be able to help other people and their families. Being in the medical field is the perfect way to do so.

There have been very few families that haven't been affected by cancer in some way, shape, form, or fashion, whether it be the person themselves, a family member, or a friend. Cancer is an extreme hardship for the people who have or had it and for their friends and family. Cancer causes the loss of many loved ones, but thanks to the development of research and technology, surviving cancer is much more likely than it was before. Kentucky especially has a significant cancer problem, with more than 30,000 new cases of cancer and over 10,000 deaths each year [1]. Kentucky ranks first in the nation for cancer incidence and mortality rates [2]. Even more specifically, the Appalachian region has extremely high rates of cancer [3].

Since I was little, my great-grandmother, or as I call her, Mamaw, has been a huge influence on my life. Everyone in the family absolutely loves and adores her. When I think of a perfect person, I think about her. My cousin and I have a very strong bond with her and she has always supported everything we did. She is one of the kindest and most caring people I've ever known. From her bright white hair, beautiful icy blue eyes, and warm smile to her charismatic personality, she is just perfect. In 2016, I was only 10 years old when they told me that she was diagnosed with breast cancer. At the time, I knew what cancer was, but I didn't quite understand all of what she was going through. With the knowledge I had, though, it was still gut-wrenching when I heard the news. When I found out, I broke down into tears because I had no idea if she would be all right or not. In the end, she had to get a mastectomy, and she still continued to get screenings afterwards. After she slowly but surely started to recover, her health began to tumble downhill again. In 2018, the cancer came back and the doctors told her that stage four metastatic breast cancer had formed and spread to her lower back. Walking started to cause her pain because of the cancer in her back and she had to go through multiple stages of chemotherapy and radiation. The chemotherapy and radiation caused her to become sick. Like most cancer patients, the chemotherapy and radiation took a big toll on Mamaw. Even though the cancer tried to tear my grandmother down, she is a fighter and she stayed strong through the process. I am so grateful for how technology and treatments have advanced over the last few years; this helped my grandmother and others live more of their lives. Because of this technology, the cancer has significantly shrunk since then and the doctors said she can live the rest of her regular life expectancy, even though she will continue to take a chemotherapy pill for the rest of her life.

My mother also had cancer. The first time she was diagnosed with cervical cancer was long before I was even born. Because of the cancer, she had to have the bottom part of her cervix removed. My mother was told that she could not have kids because of this, but later on she became pregnant with me. My mother has always called me her miracle baby. Since she had no cervix, she had to stay on bed rest for five months while she was pregnant with me. The doctors had to do a C-section on my mother, but because of the scar tissue that was left behind from the cancer surgery, they had immense problems delivering me. A process that was supposed to be an hour long turned into a 22-hour-long process. Through that process, we both could have died from the delivery, but thankfully we were both in fine health. The doctor that performed the C-section said that I was in the top five hardest deliveries he had ever done and that cutting through my mom was like cutting through concrete. A few years later, my mom ran into a few more problems with cancer. I was four years old at the time, so I do not remember much about this, but I do know now that she had benign tumors in her uterus, which ended in her getting a hysterectomy.

Kentucky, especially in the eastern region, has an epidemic problem with cancer [3]. There are many causes for this: medical illiteracy, limited access to care, unhealthy lifestyles, and/or poverty. Because of medical illiteracy and poverty, many Kentuckians are not getting the proper care they need. These people may not know about or may not be able to afford cancer screenings, which help detect the early stages of cancer. To put Kentucky's poverty rates into perspective, in the US, only 14 percent of the population lives below the federal poverty level. But, over 42 percent of the population in just one of Kentucky's Appalachian counties lives under the federal poverty level [4]. Poverty influences whether or not people may be able to afford screening or treatment for cancer. Over 85 percent of the population over the age of 25 has a high school degree in the US. But, only a little over half the population in some Appalachian counties has a high school degree [4]. Education affects how people may comprehend cancer and how they understand how important cancer prevention is. In Kentucky, about one in four (23 percent) adults smoke. And smokers' risk of getting lung cancer is 11 to 14 times higher than a nonsmoker [4]. Another factor of Kentucky having high cancer rates is an unhealthy lifestyle. This includes unhealthy eating habits, little to no exercise, smoking, and more. In Kentucky about one in three adults (34 percent) is obese [5]. Obesity and being overweight correlates to 55 percent of all cancers diagnosed in women and 24 percent of all cancers diagnosed in men [6].

Cancer in Kentucky is a very serious thing and many people don't know how to reduce the likelihood of getting cancer. There are many ways you can prevent yourself from getting cancer. For one, don't use any tobacco products and stop the use of them if you currently are using. Not only do they play a big part in your likelihood of getting cancer, they are overall extremely bad for your health. Tobacco use is the number one leading preventable cause of cancer. Not only does it cause lung cancer, but based on current evidence, it can also cause cancers in the mouth, throat, voice box, esophagus, stomach, kidney, pancreas, liver, bladder, cervix, colon, and rectum. It can also cause a type of leukemia called acute myeloid leukemia [7]. A second way that you can lower your risk of getting cancer is having a healthy diet and participating in regular exercise. Being overweight or obese can increase your risk of getting cancer in many ways. Excess weight causes the body to produce and circulate higher levels of estrogen and insulin, which are hormones that can trigger cancer growth [8]. Plus, a way to stay on top of cancer is to get cancer screenings if you see any signs of cancer or you start to get certain symptoms of cancer. Cancer screenings can be used to catch cancer in its early stages and that makes the illness much easier to treat.

The crux of the matter is that in Kentucky there are very high cancer rates and we as Kentuckians need to take precautions seriously in order to lower these rates. As a whole, we need to influence others to take precautions. Some things you can do to help: Spread this information about cancer. Donate to cancer research programs as well as volunteering with cancer outreach groups. You can also donate supplies and your time to hospitals like Shriners. Many people with severe cases of cancer have to stay in hospitals and you can easily brighten someone's day by coming to see them. If you are going to a children's hospital, you can bring a package with fun activities in it, like art supplies, toys, or movies. There are so many people researching cancer and trying to find ways to cure it, but there are so many things you as a person can do to help as well. Don't ever think that you can't help because you are just one person. If every person came together to help, we would be an unstoppable force full of endless possibilities.

In conclusion, Kentucky has very high cancer rates due to a

multitude of issues. These issues include high obesity rates, medical illiteracy, tobacco use, and high poverty rates. If people prevent these issues then the cancer rates can majorly decrease and this would lead to less deaths in the long run as well. With cancer rates decreasing in such a way, it's possible that we could be promised a brighter tomorrow.

"All I ask is this: Do something. Try something. Speaking out, showing up, writing a letter, a check, a strongly worded email. Pick a cause—there are few unworthy ones. And nudge yourself past the brink of tacit support to action. Once a month, once a year, or just once. . . . Even just learning enough about a subject so you can speak against an opponent eloquently makes you an unusual person. Start with that."

—Joss Whedon

REFERENCES

1. "Cancer Statistics Center: Kentucky at a Glance," American Cancer Society, accessed 2021, https://cancerstatisticscenter.cancer.org/#!/state/Kentucky.

2. R. L. Siegel et al., "Cancer Statistics, 2021," *CA: A Cancer Journal for Clinicians* 71, no. 1 (January–February 2021): 7–33, https://acsjournals.onlinelibrary.wiley.com/doi/10.3322/caac.21654.

3. S. D. Rodriguez et al., "A Social-Ecological Review of Cancer Disparities in Kentucky," *Southern Medical Journal* 111, no. 4 (April 2018): 213–219, https://www.ncbi.nlm.nih.gov/pmc/articles/PMC5935122/.

4. "Cancer Kills Kentuckians at Highest Rate (Update)," North American Association of Central Cancer Registries, updated March 28, 2016, https://www.naaccr.org/cancer-kills-kentuckians-at-highest-rate/.

5. M. Richardson, "Kentucky Ranks Eighth-Worst State for Obesity," *Owensboro Times*, updated February 13, 2019, https://www.owensborotimes.com/life/health-wellness/2019/02/kentucky-ranks-eighth-worst-state-for-obesity/.

6. "Cancers Associated with Overweight and Obesity Make Up 40 Percent of Cancers Diagnosed in the United States," Centers for Disease Control and Prevention, accessed 2017, https://www.cdc.gov/media/releases/2017/p1003-vs-cancer-obesity.html.

7. "Cancers Linked to Tobacco Use Make Up 40 Percent of All Cancers Diagnosed in the United States," Centers for Disease Control and Prevention, accessed 2016, https://www.cdc.gov/media/releases/2016/p1110-vital-signs-cancer-tobacco.html.

8. "Diet, Exercise, and Your Cancer Risk," American Cancer Society, accessed 2019, https://www.cancer.org/latest-news/diet-exercise-and-your-cancer-risk.html.

PICKPOCKETING OUR LIVES: THE GREAT THIEF OF KENTUCKY

Chezney Boothe

When we picture a thief, we usually think of a person dressed in black, creeping into our homes late at night and sifting through our things, taking what they want without remorse. Jiggling open locks, tearing through drawers, quietly tugging diamonds and money from our jewelry boxes. A menace taking away our material things and leaving us alarmed and quickly dialing our insurance companies when morning comes. We don't typically envision something that we can't even see, something impalpable and inhuman like a disease brewing up inside of us or someone we love. This is what cancer is to me: a thief, pilfering through our lives and ripping away things that cannot be replaced. Instead of a few necklaces or a bundle of cash, it rips away things that are intangible and irreplaceable. Cancer has no preference; family, friends, futures . . . it can and will take away anything we hold dear.

My name is Chezney Boothe. I am a sophomore at Hazard High School in Perry County, Kentucky. I'm the typical ambitious high school "smart kid": I've been the captain of our academic team since elementary school, I maintain a straight-A report card, I have good relationships with my teachers; the typical definition. My aspirations are exactly what one would expect: I plan to leave my small town one day to go to a big college, graduate with a double major, and go on to medical school to become a doctor. It's not to fit the mold, however. Neither is it for the money, or even to put my intellect to use. This is what others expect, but the truth is that I am nothing more than the culmination of my relationships with others. My mom encouraged me to always do my very best and help others along the way, my dad showed me how to avoid and overcome the obstacles set by others, and my friends taught me how to be supportive while also taking care of myself. It is for the love of these people and the influence their personalities have had upon mine that I developed a strong need, an insatiable drive, to help others; to leave the world better off than it was when I arrived.

Taking this into consideration, it is unsurprising that seeing how my community and others like it are suffering because of conditions like cancer is torturous. Nearly everyone I know has had a loved one who either endured through cancer or didn't make it. I, myself, have the typical story when asked "How has cancer affected you?": My family was made up of coal miners and tobacco users who were exposed to toxins for too long out of necessity or addiction and later developed lung cancer, throat cancer, or pneumoconiosis. In addition, I've had an uncle who had skin cancer, a cousin with colon cancer, and my maternal grandfather had prostate cancer twice. Not even these, however, are what I think of when I think about the effect cancer has had on me; these relatives died or recovered before I was even born, save for my grandpa, who recovered while I was still too young to remember. It is odd, though, that I mourn most a woman whom I never even knew.

My paternal grandmother was diagnosed with colon cancer in 1992 following a routine colonoscopy. She had surgery not long after diagnosis and, with the help of chemotherapy, her cancer went into remission about a year afterward. My dad and her family were overjoyed, of course, until 1995, when sudden back pain sent her to the hospital for testing. They learned that the cancer had come back, except this time in her lymph nodes. She started treatment immediately, but after a few months, nothing had worked. Her doctor, very respected in the area and elsewhere, managed to get her into a clinical trial for a cancer treatment at Vanderbilt University. He was so well respected, in fact, that he convinced the trial officials to send her treatment to him so that he could administer it and she didn't have to go to Nashville every week. The only problem, though, was that she had no idea whether she was receiving the actual treatment or the placebo. Either way, it, like the other treatments, wasn't working, and she passed away a few months later. Since she died almost a decade before I was born, I thought that I wasn't affected. But I now see that the little things over the years proved that it wasn't how I was influenced that would lead me to mourn; it was the ways in which I wasn't.

I always thought it was strange when other kids at school would mention having two sets of grandparents (my dad's dad had died in 2001 from heart disease), or even have both show up to family events at school like grandparents' day lunches. I eventually saw pictures of my paternal grandparents in my mother's scrapbooks and heard my parents offhandedly mention them, but I usually just shrugged it off and moved on. I learned more in the next few years, and even became able to connect with them, in a way. My dad would comment that the way I was lying on the floor while watching television was exactly like the way his dad would have done, or that my love of reading reminded him of his mom. It wasn't until Memorial Day a few years ago that I even considered what I had lost. I had gone to the cemetery with my dad to deliver flowers to their grave, and, while he said a small prayer over them, I suddenly started to cry. I had no idea why. *I didn't even know these people*, I thought, and the thought made me sob even harder.

Ever since then, I've thought about what I never got to have. What cancer *stole* from me: the opportunity of knowing my grandmother, a woman whom I know—though only at second hand—to have been wonderful. I often feel as though I am not entitled to my grief, because she was never in my life. The fact is, though, that she *has* shaped my life, whether through my dad's parenting ethic or my efforts to become someone of whom she could have been proud. It is the ways in which she hasn't touched my life, however, that I mourn; I mourn for the person I could have become had I known her. I would have been better, no doubt. Perhaps I would have been more compassionate, or more responsible, or more forgiving. I could have been *more*. I'll never know, though, because the moments we could have had, the time we could have spent together, the ways in which I could have learned from her, an *entire relationship* . . . all gone, torn away by a disease no one ever saw coming.

In hindsight, it is no surprise that so many of my family members have suffered from cancer. After all, Kentucky was ranked number one in both cancer incidence and mortality rates in 2021 [1]. But what causes this? One of the largest contributors to cancer cases in Kentucky is the engagement by Kentuckians in cancer risk behaviors. According to the Centers for Disease Control and Prevention (CDC), nearly one-fourth (23.4 percent) of adults in Kentucky reported smoking cigarettes in 2018. This trend will only increase, as 29 percent of high school students reported using tobacco products [2]. The extreme rates of tobacco use are more than reflected in cancer death rates, considering lung and bronchus cancer has the highest death rate of all cancer cases (34.8 per

100,000 population), significantly more than the second-highest (female breast cancer at 19.8 per 100,000 population) [3].

Kentucky also has a very high rate of adult obesity, with 36.5 percent of adults reporting being obese in 2019 [4]. Poor diet and a sedentary lifestyle have been linked to several cancers, including colorectal, post-menopausal breast, uterine, esophageal, kidney, and pancreatic. However, it is not obesity itself that becomes a risk factor for cancer; it is the side effects and affected processes associated with it. The long-term inflammation associated with large amounts of body fat damages cells, and increased resistance to insulin (and subsequent inflated concentrations of hormones like estrogen) have been linked to cancer as well [5].

Finally, more region-specific causes of cancer in Kentucky are exposure to toxic chemicals and coal dust. For decades, coal mining was one of the most prevalent industries in Kentucky, but now research has shown that exposure to toxins such as coal dust is linked to various lung ailments, most commonly pneumoconiosis (known colloquially as "black lung disease") and lung cancer [6]. The aforementioned statistic regarding lung and bronchus cancer mortality is most likely due to a combination of tobacco use and occupational risks associated with coal mining. Coal dust is certainly not the only environmental factor associated with cancer, however; tests of public drinking water systems performed by the Kentucky Energy and Environment Cabinet showed that half had rates of per- and polyfluoroalkyl substances (PFAS), specifically perfluorooctanoic acid (PFOA; known also as C8), that are much higher than what is considered safe by the Environmental Protection Agency [7]. Chemicals belonging to the PFAS family have been linked to increased risks of various cancers, including kidney and testicular, as well as a host of other health defects [8].

There are numerous cancer risks in the daily lives of Kentuckians, which will all need to be considered individually in efforts to reduce them. One incredibly important measure that could be taken to reduce the high cancer rates in Kentucky is education. Beginning as early as elementary school, health class curricula should include more engaging and thorough standards regarding cancer prevention and screening, focused particularly on the health risk behaviors most prevalent in Kentucky (i.e., smoking, poor diet, and lack of exercise). Kids are more open to new information when they are younger, so the earlier the better. Another more overarching cause of cancer is the systemic problem of poverty. In 2020, the rate of poverty in Kentucky was 16.3 percent of the population [9]. It is a well-established fact that poverty contributes to nutritional issues such as poor diet and obesity [10]—two major risk factors for cancer. Cheaper foods typically have much less nutritional value (and healthy foods can be very expensive), so addressing poverty itself could have a very positive effect on cancer rates in Kentucky. Whether this be through legislation to provide financial stimulus or government-funded community outreach programs that provide healthy food to families in need, the effort would be worth it. Another cause of cancer, environmental carcinogens, cannot be fixed with the improvement of financial situations or education; the only way to address this problem would be with legislation focusing on environmental regulations and protections, as well as programs to provide safer drinking water.

There is no doubt that the cancer disparities in Kentucky are taking a toll. From high rates of all types to the high mortality rate, Kentuckians are being torn apart as their families, friends, futures, opportunities, and lives are being stolen from them. It's already been decades since the work for a treatment began, but there's a long way to go; statistics are becoming more and more heartbreaking. The best option for containment right now is prevention, something for which we will all have to push. If we work together to prevent and destroy this disease, we can create a world where kids have all of their grandparents at school events, sons and daughters don't have to watch their parents die before their time, we never have to wonder who will be next, and the question of "if" we will get cancer never becomes a "when." We can create a world in which cancer has no more power and never steals another life.

REFERENCES

1. R. L. Siegel et al., "Cancer Statistics, 2021," *CA: A Cancer Journal for Clinicians* 71, no. 1 (January–February 2021): 7–33, https://acsjournals.onlinelibrary.wiley.com/doi/10.3322/caac.21654.

2. "Extinguishing the Tobacco Epidemic in Kentucky," Centers for Disease Control and Prevention, accessed 2021, https://www.cdc.gov/tobacco/about/osh/state-fact-sheets/kentucky/index.html.

3. "USCS Data Visualizations," Centers for Disease Control and Prevention, accessed 2020, https://gis.cdc.gov/Cancer/USCS/DataViz.html.

4. "Adult Obesity Prevalence Maps," Centers for Disease Control and Prevention, accessed 2021, https://www.cdc.gov/obesity/data/prevalence-maps.html.

5. D. Underferth, "How Does Obesity Cause Cancer?" University of Texas MD Anderson Cancer Center, accessed 2020, https://www.mdanderson.org/publications/focused-on-health/how-does-obesity-cause-cancer.h27Z1591413.html.

6. "Coal Mine Dust Exposures and Associated Health Outcomes: A Review of Information Published Since 1995," Centers for Disease Control and Prevention, accessed 2011, https://www.cdc.gov/niosh/docs/2011-172/pdfs/2011-172.pdf.

7. "Evaluation of Kentucky Community Drinking Water for Per- & Poly-Fluoroalkyl Substances," Kentucky Energy and Environment Cabinet, Department for Environmental Protection, Division of

Water, accessed 2019, https://eec.ky.gov/Documents%20for%20 URLs/PFAS%20Drinking%20Water%20Report%20Final.pdf.

8. "Potential Health Effects of PFAS Chemicals," Centers for Disease Control and Prevention, accessed 2020, https://www.atsdr.cdc.gov/ pfas/health-effects/index.html.

9. "Kentucky Report—2020," Talk Poverty, accessed 2021, https://talk-poverty.org/state-year-report/kentucky-2020-report/.

10. D. Khullar and D.A. Chokshi, "Health, Income, & Poverty: Where We Are & What Could Help: Health Policy Brief," Health Affairs, October 4, 2018, https://www.healthaffairs.org/ do/10.1377/hpb20180817.901935/full/?source=soc WB-team-fb-rollout-20191009.

CANCER:
A DESTRUCTIVE DISEASE

Harley Bowen

Cancer, a devastating disease that strikes fear into many people just hearing the name, is a disease that has plagued the population of the state of Kentucky for a long time. My name is Harley Bowen and I am a sophomore at East Carter High School in Grayson, Kentucky. I am a student in the second cohort of students at the Markey Cancer Center Appalachian Career Training in Oncology Program. I am a collective 4.0 GPA unweighted student and I have always had a fascination with biology, anatomy, and medical terminology since I've been young. My sought-after career is to be an orthopedic surgeon or possibly an oncological pathologist. I wish to be an orthopedic surgeon or just in the medical field in some way, shape, or form because I've been able to see firsthand the effect healthcare providers have on an individual and their family. Today I will be sharing my personal experience with a disease that almost everyone has heard of and had some kind of personal experience with, and that disease is cancer. Cancer is caused by a mutation within the genes that control the growth of cells, and when a mutation within a cell occurs, it can create a growth of cells called a tumor. Tumors can be classified into two main categories: benign (don't spread and usually harmless) and malignant (can spread to other parts of the body and can invade and kill nearby tissue). These tumors can invade or spread to local or distant areas within the body and ultimately lead to death. In this essay I will be talking about three main points: My personal experiences with cancer, why I believe that cancer is such a prevalent issue in our state, and ways I believe we could all work together to combat this awful disease.

My family has a long history with cancer and it can be traced back as far as four generations in my family. Two of my great-aunts were diagnosed with cancer. One of them, who had never smoked a cigarette, was diagnosed suddenly with lung cancer, and died at the age of 91. You could take into consideration her age, so cancer may not have been the final deciding factor, but she was in great health before being diagnosed with lung cancer. My other great-aunt was diagnosed with breast cancer and it ended up coming back on three separate occasions. My grandfather on my mom's side of the family was diagnosed with prostate cancer, which he thankfully recovered from. This experience with cancer was a little more recent and occurred very suddenly. My mom, dad, and I were sitting in the living room when we got a phone call. When we answered the phone, we received the news that my grandfather had been diagnosed with prostate cancer and that his surgery was set to be done a week after the phone call. Thankfully, he made a full recovery because it was found early, and he is still a pastor in Georgetown. His brother was also diagnosed with prostate cancer, which seems to be common on my mom's side of the family.

My grandmother on my dad's side of the family was diagnosed with thyroid cancer and she ended up having her thyroid removed because of it. I remember when we learned that my grandmother had cancer. We were on a train ride through the Red River Gorge, and nearing the end of it we started to realize something was wrong. It was three months prior to her diagnosis with thyroid cancer when we noticed that she started to get choked on food more and more often. When we were at the end of the train ride, we got off of the train and went to go and get food. Once again, she had gotten choked. We just thought that it was her not being careful when she ate so we didn't think too much of it. When we got back home after the train ride, though, another series of events led us to the diagnosis of early-stage thyroid cancer. We were eating, and once again, she choked. We took her to the hospital when she got choked the last time because the food wouldn't go down on its own, leading us to know that something wrong was going on. The doctor was curious as to what was going on so they took some X-rays, and to everyone's surprise, she had a small tumor in her thyroid. It was only a small and early-stage tumor that hadn't metastasized, so they were able to do surgery on it. She ended up making a full recovery and is still alive today. I still wonder though what would have happened had we not taken her to the hospital when we did. In addition to everyone talked about so far, two of my great-uncles on my mother's side of the family were diagnosed with colon cancer as well. Thankfully they were able to make recoveries, like most of the people in my family that have had cancer, and live their lives just like they did before. Finally, I had two first cousins on my dad's side of the family that died of breast cancer. The common themes seem to be that my mom's side of the family has had a history of prostate cancer, and my dad's side has had a history of breast cancer. Needless to say, cancer has run its toll through our family and has come through both my mom's and my dad's sides of the family.

Next I will be discussing why I believe cancer impacts the citizens of Kentucky so harshly as opposed to any other state and the causes associated with the high rates of cancer within our state. I believe that multiple reasons can be credited for Kentucky's cancer problem. Many of the reasons and possible causes that I will list are preventable and should be avoided at all costs, such as obesity and tobacco use. If you can, it is best to try to limit your exposure to carcinogenic chemicals and to try to eliminate risk factors that can increase your risk of developing cancer. One reason I believe Kentucky is harshly affected by cancer is the industries in the state. Some of Kentucky's biggest industries are the generation of electricity through the burning of coal, coal mining, and farming. Careers in all three of these industries set people at risk of breathing in harsh, cancer-causing chemicals such as asbestos, chromium, and dichlorodiphenyltrichloroethane (also known as DDT), which is an insecticide. DDT was first introduced in 1940 as the first synthetic insecticide, and it was initially used to combat malaria, typhus, and other insect-borne human diseases among military and civilians [1]. These carcinogenic chemicals were once thought of as safe until it was found years later that they could lead to serious health complications. It has been proven that these chemicals are carcinogenic, and prolonged exposure to them could cause cancer.

A second reason I believe that Kentucky is affected very harshly by cancer is our obesity rate. The obesity rate for Kentucky is the fifth highest among all 50 states, coming in at roughly 37 percent of Kentucky's citizens. This means that almost 2 out of 5 people in the state are obese. Out of the entire population, if you used this number to find roughly how many obese people are in the state of Kentucky, you would find that there are 1,653,900 obese people in Kentucky out of 4.47 million citizens [2]. Personally for me, this is shocking and it really puts into perspective the things that go unnoticed within the community because if you look around you while out in public you'll notice a lot more people who are overweight and obese than you realize. I would even go as far as to say that obesity is a preventable epidemic within the state of Kentucky, and it's important for the health and survival of our citizens that we help to increase knowledge about the negative effects of obesity and the risks involved, such as various cancers and other major physical ailments [3]. Being obese can raise the risk of several cancers, and among these are breast cancer, colon cancer, kidney cancer, ovarian cancer, and esophageal cancer [3]. These are only a few out of a high variety of different cancers that obesity can cause.

A third reason I believe that cancer affects Kentucky's population so much is smoking, and the number of smokers in Kentucky. Research shows that 23.6 percent of adults in the state of Kentucky smoke cigarettes [4]. So, roughly 1 in 4 people in Kentucky smoke cigarettes. Cigarettes are widely known to be cancer-causing and ultimately terrible for you. Cigarettes contain up to 4,000 different chemicals, and among those 4,000, about 70 of them are carcinogenic, or cancer-causing. Cigarettes don't just harm the people using them, but also the people around them. A silent killer is secondhand smoke, which can also expose others who don't smoke cigarettes to some of the same carcinogens and health risks that smokers expose themselves to [5].

And lastly, my fourth and final reason is genetics. Cancer can be caused by a multitude of external factors, but it can also be attributed to genetics and family lineage. This cause is less common than other causes listed and it's not an external factor that causes it, but it could be a reason that cancer may affect people of Kentucky so harshly. Hereditary cancer is defined as "a type of inherited disorder in which there is a higher-than-normal risk of certain types of cancer" [6]. The difference between sporadic versus hereditary cancer is that with a sporadic mutation that causes cancer, you are not already at a predisposition to have cancer, but rather the mutation occurs after you're born. Hereditary cancer on the other hand is passed down through your family and puts you at a predisposition to develop cancer. As I stated before, my great-aunt was diagnosed with lung cancer that would eventually take her life, even though she had never smoked a cigarette one day in her 91 years of living. This could have just been a case where genetics was the cause of the cancer, but more likely it was the result of a sporadic mutation. Possibly, though, the case in which my grandfather had prostate cancer could have been due to an inherited gene mutation. Two common types of cancer that occur as a result of genetics are breast cancer and prostate cancer [7].

It goes without saying that Kentucky is at a disadvantage for the development of cancer because of the industries that release cancer-causing chemicals into the air, because of the obesity rates, and because people are not living the healthiest lifestyles. The obesity rates could be attributed to a lack of education in Kentucky and to the number of fast-food restaurants, which seem to be everywhere. Because of the number of fast-food restaurants in Kentucky, I would go as far as saying that the fast-food industry is targeting the people of Kentucky. The fast-food restaurants all throughout the state of Kentucky put people at a bad disadvantage as far as overall health and it increases the risk of developing cancer. It's a sad way that restaurant chains make money because others are suffering the consequences. Fast-food restaurants have become widely available all around Kentucky; in 2015, Kentucky ranked first in the nation for the number of fast-food restaurants serving the population, coming in at 4.12 restaurants per 10,000 people [8]. The lack of education in Kentucky is a very large issue all throughout the state and especially throughout the Appalachian region of Kentucky. This is because schooling and education isn't as valued in this part of Kentucky for most people and families. With a lack of education comes a lack of cancer literacy, which is very important to help people understand cancer and the risk factors associated with it. Education can be one of the largest preventive measures in fighting this disease as it will leave you more equipped to understand the causes of cancer and risk factors that can lead to the development of cancer.

Finally, I will talk about some things that can be done to address cancer in Kentucky. One of the first things I believe would prove helpful is to go out and educate people about the disease in your community as this would help to increase cancer literacy. I'm not saying that you have to go out and announce to everyone in your town that cancer is a huge and prevalent issue in Kentucky, but instead just tell a couple of close friends and family members. Maybe if your message reaches them in a positive way, they'll go out and tell their other friends and their family members about the cancer issues in Kentucky and some of the biggest causes of it. This way would be good due to the fact that just telling a couple of people could end up having an impact on hundreds of people's lives. I believe that a second way to address the issue of cancer in Kentucky is through social media and social platforms. I know most people have some form of social media, whether it's Instagram, Facebook, Snapchat, etc. I believe this would be effective because this would let the issue be widely known and it could allow people to tell others about the cancer issue within Kentucky, and then they could educate themselves and others on this topic that affects almost every citizen in the state in some way, shape, or form. We could also keep doing what our town and a lot of other towns do to raise awareness for cancer. We could have annual runs and fundraisers to help raise money for cancer research and care, which is something that we do in my hometown of Grayson. In my hometown we have annual runs that raise money for cancer research; we do two 5k runs each year. Also, around certain times of the year our small businesses take up donations for funding for cancer research at St. Jude's children's hospital. I believe this would be very beneficial in a lot of other towns across not only Kentucky, but around the entire country. With other events that raise cancer awareness, we would be able to further push forward this fight against cancer and hopefully raise awareness for the disease.

Cancer is an epidemic in this state that seems to affect everyone in some way, and it's a fight that no one person will be able to win alone. We need to take steps to recognize that this disease is a large issue within both our own community and all around the state, and that there are things that we can all do to come together and combat this terrible disease. This has been my story with cancer. I hope that you learned something from this and took away one main point: cancer is a prevalent issue in our state and around the country, and it should not be ignored. Also take away that there are many things that can be done to raise awareness for this disease and take preventive measures against it, such as living a healthier lifestyle, helping to raise cancer literacy within your town, and explaining the risks to people who live a high-risk lifestyle, teaching them things they can do to stop putting themselves at a higher risk for developing cancer. I want to leave you with a question to think on and incorporate into your life personally: What can you do to help combat this epidemic in Kentucky and what steps will you take to do so?

REFERENCES

1. "DDT: A Brief History and Status," US Environmental Protection Agency, 2021, https://www.epa.gov/ingredients-used-pesticide-products/ddt-brief-history-and-status.

2. A. Cross, "Adult Obesity in Kentucky Reaches All-Time High of 36.6 Percent in US; Doctor Says Insurance Needs to Start Covering Obesity Prevention," Kentucky Health News, 2019, https://ci.uky.edu/kentuckyhealthnews/2019/09/16/adult-obesity-in-ky-reaches-all-time-high-of-36-6-fifth-in-u-s-doctor-says-insurance-needs-to-start-covering-obesity-prevention/.

3. "Obesity and Cancer," National Cancer Institute, accessed 2021, https://www.cancer.gov/about-cancer/causes-prevention/risk/obesity/obesity-fact-sheet.

4. "America's Health Rankings Annual Report," United Health Foundation, 2020, https://www.americashealthrankings.org/explore/annual/measure/Smoking/state/KY.

5. "Secondhand Smoke (SHS) Facts," Centers for Disease Control and Prevention, 2021, https://www.cdc.gov/tobacco/data_statistics/fact_sheets/secondhand_smoke/general_facts/index.htm.

6. "Heredity Cancer Syndrome," National Cancer Institute, 2021, https://www.cancer.gov/publications/dictionaries/cancer-terms/def/hereditary-cancer-syndrome.

7. "Family Cancer Syndromes," American Cancer Society, 2021, https://www.cancer.org/cancer/cancer-causes/genetics/family-cancer-syndromes.html.

8. C. Bowling, "Kentucky Takes Top Honors (?) When It Comes to Fast-Food Restaurants," *Louisville Business First*, March 6, 2015, https://www.bizjournals.com/louisville/news/2015/03/06/kentucky-takes-top-honors-when-it-comes-to-fast.html.

CANCER IS ONE WORD

Kassidy Burke

"There were so many slogans that I liked, I found it really hard to pick just one. In the end, I chose 'Cancer Is a Word, Not a Sentence.' This fits with what is behind our efforts to create Cancer Health. We are looking to help change the dialogue around what it means when you hear the word cancer. For so long, if you heard cancer, it was synonymous with dying. Today that is no longer true. With new innovative treatments helping battle cancer like never before, it's time to stop treating cancer like a sentence. Like the message embedded in our logo, it's time to say 'Can Heal!'"
—Ian Anderson, President and COO, Smart + Strong

Cancer. That's such a scary word for something with only six letters. But why is it so terrifying? Maybe because you know it's an illness? Maybe because you know someone or maybe more than one person who has had this terrible sickness?

I am Kassidy Burke and I currently reside in Lawrence County, Kentucky, which is one of the secluded Appalachian counties. I am currently a sophomore at Lawrence County High School, and I am 16 years old. Cancer has greatly impacted me, my family, and my community. Lawrence County is a very close community, and we strive to help everyone. My community has suffered greatly from the deadly disease known as cancer.

Our community is very involved in October's Breast Cancer Awareness Month. If sporting events are going on, everyone in the stands, on the field, and on the sidelines is dressed in all pink to support the cause. There are always Breast Cancer Awareness Month shirts for sale to raise money for people who suffer from breast cancer and to make everyone an advocate for those fighting the illness.

One person in particular always raises the most money for Breast Cancer Awareness Month, not because she has breast cancer, but because she has brain cancer. Knowing her has greatly impacted my life and how I view my health. My family and I were very close with her and watched her go through tremendous pain. She has to travel to Duke University and now Florida for her treatment because no one in our area can assist her with her illness. Watching her live her best life even with the illness is astonishing. She has taught me not to ask for pity but instead to ask for compassion. She has also taught me that even though my life could end at any time, it is best to live life to the fullest each day. Just this one person with cancer helps raise the Kentucky average for cases. Just in Kentucky, there will be an estimated 30,270 new cases of cancer in 2021 and 10,090 deaths [1]. Although cancer rates in Kentucky are high, the cancer rates are highest in the Appalachian area of Kentucky [2].

The cancer problem in Kentucky is worse in Appalachian Kentucky, I believe, because the Appalachian counties in Kentucky are so secluded, impoverished, and lack basic general knowledge, so it is harder for people in the area to seek treatment. Appalachian Kentucky is one of the poorest places in the United States. With gas prices rising and the average income for Appalachian Kentuckians being $26,653, it is very difficult for residents to afford overnight accommodations along with travel expenses and medical bills [3]. Most cancer treatment plans occur over multiple times a month, making treatments unaffordable for Kentuckians. Also having a lack of general basic knowledge about cancer will make the cancer rates rise; not knowing the early signs, effects, and how to avoid cancer will worsen the cancer rates because no one would know how to detect the early symptoms of cancer and how to avoid the disease.

Cancer in Appalachian Kentucky is so detrimental because many people are unwilling to give up their bad habits and/or because people do not want to go to the doctor after showing symptoms. Pollution, cigarettes/vaping, obesity, and many other environmental factors can cause cancer. Cigarettes and other nicotine products are highly addictive and carry chemicals that may cause cancer. Among 250 chemicals that are known to be harmful in cigarette smoke, at least 69 of them can cause cancer [4]. With these cancer-causing chemicals and terrible habits of vaping, smoking, and/or chewing tobacco, the rates of lung cancer may increase. But, despite people engaging in risky behaviors, lung cancer death rates have declined in Kentucky [5]. The overall cancer rates in the US are also declining [6].

Ways that we could decrease cancer rates in Appalachian Kentucky would be by increasing cancer literacy, having affordable insurance and treatment, and providing more local healthcare. By teaching people about what cancer is and the early signs of cancer, people will have a better understanding of how to detect cancer and how to help themselves. Also, telling Kentuckians the ways you can develop cancer will help increase their cancer knowledge. Having more affordable insurance and treatment will also help decrease cancer rates in Appalachian Kentucky. If Kentuckians can afford treatment plans given by their doctor, they are more than likely to go seek treatment. Having more local healthcare facilities would decrease the cancer rates because there could be more cancer screenings offered in our communities and more early stages of cancer found, leading to better health outcomes. If more facilities existed, those with cancer could also get their treatments closer to their homes.

Cancer in Appalachian Kentucky is worse than in any other part of Kentucky. By increasing cancer literacy, making more affordable healthcare and treatment, and having more local healthcare facilities, there could be a decrease in cancer rates over time. To be sure, we have to make changes if we want to see cancer rates decline in Appalachian Kentucky. And I know we all do. We don't want any more of our family and friends to hear the one dreadful word "cancer" again.

REFERENCES

1. "Cancer Statistics Center: Kentucky at a Glance," American Cancer Society, accessed 2021, https://cancerstatisticscenter.cancer.org/#!/state/Kentucky.

2. S. D. Rodriguez et al., "A Social-Ecological Review of Cancer Disparities in Kentucky," *Southern Medical Journal* 111, no. 4 (April 2018): 213–219, https://www.ncbi.nlm.nih.gov/pmc/articles/PMC5935122/.

3. "American Community Survey 5-Year Data (2009–2019)," US Census Bureau, 2020, https://www.census.gov/data/developers/data-sets/acs-5year.html.

4. "Harms of Cigarette Smoking and Health Benefits of Quitting," National Cancer Institute, 2017, https://www.cancer.gov/about-cancer/causes-prevention/risk/tobacco/cessation-fact-sheet.

5. E. Coghill, "Kentucky Had the Highest Lung-Cancer Mortality Rate in the Nation from 2013–2017, Although the Rate is Falling," Norton Healthcare, February 5, 2020, https://nortonhealthcare.com/news/lung-cancer-improvements-lead-overall-drop-in-u-s-cancer-death-rate/.

6. S. Radcliffe, "Cancer Deaths Are Down Nearly 30%: Here's Why," Healthline, 2020, https://www.healthline.com/health-news/cancer-deaths-are-down-30-percent.

BRINGING CANCER TO A HALT IN KENTUCKY

Caylee Caudill

Heartbreak. A feeling that most people dealing with cancer have probably felt, and especially those who have to watch the disease take its course on their loved ones. Every chemo treatment, every hospital visit, and, unfortunately, every death takes a huge toll on everyone involved. It is, of course, awful to ever have to fight for your life due to cancer, but it is also terrible for those who have to watch it happen. Sadly, many people in Eastern Kentucky have had to deal with the loss of a loved one due to cancer and, more often than not, deal with the illness themselves. Kentucky has a cancer death rate of 191.2 per 100,000 people [1]. This statistic is drastically different compared to somewhere like Utah that has a death rate of only 123.9 per 100,000 people [2]. Kentucky has some of the highest cancer rates in the US, especially in the more eastern region [3, 4]. This large number of deaths shouldn't be the "norm" in Kentucky. There are several reasons as to why these rates are so high: lack of healthcare resources, poverty, obesity, tobacco use, the mindset of Kentuckians, and the influence tobacco and other cancer-causing substances have on our youth. Things need to change or Kentuckians will go on facing the repercussions of this horrible disease. I will discuss my own cancer experiences, the causes of our cancer plight, and changes that need to be made to lower Kentucky's cancer rate.

Hello, my name is Caylee Caudill and I am from Johnson County in the Appalachian region of Kentucky. I live in a small town called Paintsville and I go to school at Johnson Central High School as a sophomore. I am also a member of the Appalachian Career Training in Oncology (ACTION) Program at the Markey Cancer Center in Lexington, Kentucky. My region is significantly affected by cancer, which is why I am so lucky to be involved in a program that strives to educate the younger generation on the effects of cancer. This program has helped to inform me on cancer statistics, how cancer affects Kentucky specifically, and how I can help increase outreach in my community. My time in the program has also made me realize that I may want to pursue a career in cancer research. I didn't really know that I wanted to be involved in the healthcare field in my earlier years. I wanted to be a professional basketball player, then a teacher, then a chef, as well as many other careers. Once you get to high school you actually have to start deciding what classes you want to take and what careers you want to pursue. I think it was my mother's career as a nurse that pushed me in the direction of the healthcare field. She has been a nurse for eight years and is currently in the nurse practitioner program at Northern Kentucky University. She and my father are two of the most devoted and hardworking people I have ever met and they have always supported me in the choices I make. I am grateful to have them in my life and to have their help in participating in the ACTION program. Seeing how hard my mother works to help others has made me realize that I would like to do the same. It just so happens that I quite enjoy learning about all aspects of the medical field from anatomy to even medical terminology. I have decided now that I want to become an orthopedic surgeon possibly specializing in oncology.

Cancer runs in my family and it has made a huge impact on my life. My great-grandmother and grandfather died from cancer. I was very close with them both so it was really hard for me when they passed away. Even my mother had a lump in her breast when I was young and it was a very scary and stressful time for my family. She was scared and so was I, but, luckily, because of her career in the healthcare field, she knew to get regular screenings and got the lump removed before it progressed. Most people in Appalachia aren't so lucky.

First of all, one of the biggest reasons that Eastern Kentucky is so infected with cancer is the general lack of healthcare resources due to poverty. Forty-two percent of the population in Kentucky's Appalachian counties lives below the federal poverty level compared to only 14 percent of the US population [3]. This rate of poverty leads to the lack of regular health screenings, checkups, and general medical care due to a number of reasons. One of the largest reasons is that many people in Kentucky are uninsured. One in ten Kentucky adults ages 18–64 reported being uninsured [5]. As a result, Kentuckians aren't getting the healthcare and education opportunities needed to live a healthy lifestyle. Furthermore, many are afraid of going to the doctor for fear of not being able to afford it. Hospital bills can effectively bankrupt a family, and many in Appalachia don't have the resources to pay for all of these expenses.

Second, along with the lack of healthcare resources, people also aren't educated enough on how to stay healthy and keep their bodies in good condition. Obesity and other health issues can occur as a result. In 2018, Kentucky's obesity rate was 36.6 percent [6]. Obesity can make a person more likely to develop cancer in the future, and this is a real issue in Kentucky that contributes to our high cancer rates. One of the running theories as to why obesity leads to cancer is that the visceral fat surrounding your organs leads to inflammation [7]. This inflammation can cause a lack of oxygen to your cells and tissues and affect the way that your body deals with certain chemicals and hormones [7]. Obesity is very common in the Appalachian part of Kentucky most likely because of the lack of education around the topic. Not knowing how to take care of your body in the first place can lead to poor health in the future, such as obesity and possibly cancer. Sadly, being informed can be the difference between staying healthy and becoming ill. This is a real problem in our area.

Third, commercial tobacco is a huge source of the horrible cancer rates in Appalachian Kentucky. The tobacco industry has helped to create many jobs growing and selling tobacco products. As we all know, tobacco leads to addiction and can cause cancer. From my experience, the huge legacy that this cancerous plant has left has led to more smoking and chewing in Kentucky. As a result, cancer rates have skyrocketed in Appalachia. Lung cancer is one of the biggest issues in this area. This type of cancer contributes to 28 percent of new cancer cases in Kentucky and around a third of cancer-related deaths [3]. Tobacco, being one of the leading causes of lung cancer, has helped to contribute to the excessive number of cancer cases in Kentucky.

Fourth, another big reason that cancer is so common in Appalachia is the impact tobacco products have on our youth. Tobacco products are introduced to younger generations from the get-go. My school is a "tobacco-free" campus. It might be tech-nically tobacco-free, but that doesn't stop students from bringing tobacco products to school and putting a chew in while walking down the hall like it's nothing. Some teachers stop the kids and confiscate their stuff, while others will just let it slide because they don't really care. Most kids my age do not realize what the effects of tobacco actually are. If these habits do not change, it could likely lead to cancer and sometimes death. A group of students at my school started a "Don't Juul in School" campaign which initially aimed to pass a bill that banned Juuls from school campuses around Kentucky. The students involved were presented with an award from the Foundation for a Healthy Kentucky, but sadly this bill did not pass [8]. It did, however, help to pass a bill that changed the legal age to purchase tobacco products from 18 to 21. After witnessing the work that my fellow peers were doing, Senator Mitch McConnell personally strived to get the Tobacco 21 bill passed. The students even received letters from the senator congratulating them on their work. The Tobacco 21 bill can help to decrease the intake of tobacco by the younger demographic, but teenagers will still get these products in a number of ways. Most gas stations in the area do not even ID people when purchasing tobacco. Teens also receive tobacco products from older people above the legal limit. Kids give older people money to purchase it and then get their tobacco easily. This is a real problem spreading within our youth.

Finally, one of the biggest issues that I have experienced when dealing with cancer in Kentucky is the mindset of Kentuckians. I have found that is a huge problem when talking about cancer. In Appalachia, smoking is considered normal. To see someone smoking outside of Walmart or to find cigarette butts on the ground isn't out of the ordinary. Years ago, there was no talk of cigarettes and chewing tobacco being bad for you. Older generations have integrated the belief that tobacco is the "norm" into their brains and passed it down through generations. Even some of my immediate family has been smoking since they were 15 and others even earlier than that. From personal experience, some of my loved ones have had what looks like skin cancer but won't go to the doctor to get it checked. They say something like, "I'll go to the doctor when I have to." The sad truth is that, when someone absolutely has to go to the doctor, it could be too late to do anything about it. This is how a large number of Kentuckians think, which is why there are so many cancer-related deaths here.

Although there are many issues to deal with, there are some key ways that we can help to reduce cancer rates in Kentucky. One of the ways we can improve is by allowing for more free tests and screenings. As I said, poverty is one of the leading reasons why Eastern Kentucky has such high cancer rates. Making these tests and screenings available for those who can't afford them would highly increase the number of people getting regular checkups and, therefore, help decrease cancer rates in Kentucky. One of the most substantial ways we can help to change the toll cancer takes on Kentucky is by introducing cancer curriculum into schools. I can't say that I have ever had a lesson in school where I specifically learned about cancer. We need to educate our youth on the effects that using tobacco products has on your health. By reaching the youth demographic we can prevent the careless mindset around cancer from spreading to future generations. We can also help others learn how to take care of their bodies and stay healthy so that they are less likely to develop cancer. Providing education can help to inspire others to increase outreach in the community. Doing even the smallest acts can help to spread information about cancer and health which could help people lower their cancer risk.

In conclusion, some of the main causes of the enormous cancer rates in Appalachian Kentucky are the general lack of healthcare resources, the mindset of Kentuckians, and the effect that tobacco products and the generational influence of older tobacco users have on our youth. Some of the ways we can help to change this are by providing easier access to cancer tests and screenings, introducing cancer curricula into schools, and increasing cancer outreach and education in the community. We need to start the discussion on cancer so things can start to change. We need to help spread awareness any way we can, whether that be at school, work, or anywhere else. William Shakespeare once said, "To be or not to be? That is the question." With cancer that is the question—To be or not to be? To live or to die? With cancer, you don't know how your fate will pan out, but people like you and me can help to spread more awareness about this awful disease. In doing so, we can help bring more answers and we will start to hear this question less and less and, hopefully, we can bring cancer to a halt in Kentucky.

REFERENCES

1. "Cancer Statistics Center: Kentucky at a Glance," American Cancer Society, accessed 2021, https://cancerstatisticscenter.cancer.org/#!/state/Kentucky.

2. "Cancer Statistics Center: Utah at a Glance," American Cancer Society, accessed 2021, https://cancerstatisticscenter.cancer.org/#!/state/Utah.

3. "Cancer Kills Kentuckians at Highest Rate (Update)," North American Association of Central Cancer Registries, updated March 28, 2016, https://www.naaccr.org/cancer-kills-kentuckians-at-highest-rate/.

4. S. D. Rodriguez et al., "A Social-Ecological Review of Cancer Disparities in Kentucky," *Southern Medical Journal* 111, no. 4 (April 2018): 213–219, https://www.ncbi.nlm.nih.gov/pmc/articles/PMC5935122/.

5. "Kentucky Health Issues Poll: Rate of Uninsured in Kentucky Holds Steady, Concern over Losing Health Insurance Drops to 16 Percent," Foundation for a Healthy Kentucky, 2019, https://www.healthy-ky.org/newsroom/news-releases/article/282/kentucky-health-issues-poll-rate-of-uninsured-in-kentucky-holds-steady-concern-over-losing-health-insurance-drops-to-16?

6. A. Cross, "Adult Obesity in Kentucky Reaches All-Time High of 36.6 Percent in US; Doctor Says Insurance Needs to Start Covering Obesity Prevention," Kentucky Health News, 2019, https://ci.uky.edu/kentuckyhealthnews/2019/09/16/adult-obesity-in-ky-reaches-all-time-high-of-36-6-fifth-in-u-s-doctor-says-insurance-needs-to-start-covering-obesity-prevention/.

7. D. Underferth, "How Does Obesity Cause Cancer?" University of Texas MD Anderson Cancer Center, accessed 2020, https://www.mdanderson.org/publications/focused-on-health/how-does-obesity-cause-cancer.h27Z1591413.html.

8. A. K. Nelson, "JCMS Students Awarded for Anti-Vape Campaign," *Paintsville Herald,* June 1, 2019, https://www.paintsville-herald.com/news/jcms-students-awarded-for-anti-vape-campaign/article_15e89dce-84a3-11e9-a097-cf16c2c701bd.html.

CANCER: A PERSONAL STORY

Makinna Caudill

Cancer. This word affects so many families, especially in Kentucky. My name is Makinna Caudill, and I am from Salyersville, Kentucky. I attend Magoffin County High School. I'm in the graduating class of 2024. I am a part of Markey Cancer Center's Appalachian Career Training in Oncology (ACTION) Program. I am also on the tennis and volleyball team at my school. I have been interested in the medical field since I was quite young. I initially became interested in the field after my mother was diagnosed. And, because of my experience, I am passionate about working with individuals and their families who are going through this vulnerable, emotional period. Having been impacted by cancer instilled in me the deep desire to find better ways to treat this disease that so profoundly impacts the lives of so many.

This frightful disease has struck my family multiple times. My mother began to experience severe abdominal pain which lasted for several months, and through the persuasion of family and friends, she decided to visit her family practitioner, who suggested she receive a colonoscopy. After receiving her colonoscopy, my mother was diagnosed with stage three colon cancer. After learning of her diagnosis, she discussed her treatment plan with a general surgeon. The surgeon recommended a colectomy, a procedure in which a portion of the colon is removed. My mother successfully underwent the colectomy. The surgeon removed the entire tumor. However, a biopsy revealed cancer cells in surrounding lymph nodes. My mother's treatment continued as she was referred to an oncologist in Lexington, Kentucky. There, she received several chemotherapy treatments. The chemotherapy treatments ended prematurely due to the significant associated side effects, including fatigue and nausea, that my mother experienced. My mother was declared cancer free and now undergoes routine diagnostic scans and blood work to make sure the cancer does not return. Shortly after battling colon cancer, my mother discovered she had skin cancer. Fortunately, it was not melanoma. I find it intriguing that my mother's brother was also diagnosed with colon cancer when he was 44, which was the same age as my mother when she was diagnosed. He is also now cancer free.

As my understanding of cancer grew, I became increasingly devastated. Living in a small town with few specialists nearby meant my mother would have to travel to receive desirable healthcare. Some mornings I remember her leaving before I went to school. This meant my mother was forced to leave me in the care of extended relatives and family friends. Throughout this difficult journey, a good support system was essential. Someone we could always rely on was my aunt. She always was there for me whenever my mother was going through her treatments, whether it was taking me to school or dance or simply just being there for me.

Sometimes the treatments made my mother too ill to play with me. I remember her loving to watch me dance, so during times when she didn't feel well, I would always dance for her. One memory I have is doing a front roll and knocking my two front teeth out, but this didn't stop me from dancing for her for long—in just a couple days, I was back dancing.

After my mother was cancer free she looked at the preventive measures our family could take to help prevent all types of cancer. We started by eating healthier and exercising more. At the time we had very unhealthy eating habits, which is a factor that leads to colon cancer. We also discovered how important regular screenings are. Additionally, we discovered that since my mother had colon cancer at a young age, my sister and I would have to be screened once we turn 30, which is important for early detection and to be safe. Knowing your family's medical history is also important to see if certain diseases, such as cancer, are common within your family. Another important way to prevent cancer is wearing sunscreen. Wearing sunscreen prevents one of the most common and preventable cancers in the United States, skin cancer.

Along with wearing sunscreen, another measure to prevent skin cancer is to not use tanning beds. Just one tanning session can increase your chances of developing skin cancer.

In addition, another major risk factor for multiple types of cancer is obesity. Obesity is a condition in which a person has an unhealthy amount of body fat. Cancers associated with being overweight and obese make up 40 percent of cancers diagnosed in the United States. Types of cancer that are linked to obesity are breast, colorectal, uterine, kidney, head and neck, esophageal, pancreatic, endometrium, prostate, gallbladder, and thyroid cancer [1]. In Kentucky, 35 percent or more of adults are obese [2]. The two main ways to prevent obesity are exercising regularly and maintaining a healthy diet. These are two easy ways in which at least 11 types of cancer can be prevented. I realize that most small towns, such as my hometown, do not have exercise facilities or activities that involve exercising. This is why the importance of imagining new creative ways to exercise and pursuing them is crucial for your health. Something equally important to your health is maintaining a healthy, balanced diet.

Staying away from fast food, soda, and junk food is important since they are processed foods high in calories. Foods you want to eat to avoid obesity are fresh fruits and vegetables along with grain foods, starchy vegetables, and dairy.

A new trend for many teens to participate in is using e-cigarettes. E-cigarettes are essentially battery-powered smoking devices. Many teens start vaping due to peer pressure, then become addicted. In my school vaping is extremely common and seen as normal. I have witnessed my peers go through multiple disposable vapes per week. The aerosol in e-cigarettes contains cancer-causing chemicals. They have liquids inside that contain nicotine, chemicals, and flavorings [3]. E-cigarettes, often referred to as vapes, are very deceiving because the flavorings in these vapes cause teens and adults to become addicted. There was a partial flavor ban that went into effect limiting flavored cartridges. This is still a problem because the ban did not involve disposable vapes that can be purchased in multiple sorts of flavors, nor did it ban tank vapes. The commonly used "Puff Bar," which is a disposable vape, has 300 puffs in each bar, which is roughly the same as 20 cigarettes in a pack. Meaning each bar is equal to a whole pack of cigarettes. To fight the war on E-cigarettes, schools should implement a curriculum that shows students the importance of not vaping and the risks vaping can cause. If students have an understanding of the risks they have a better chance of quitting.

In the small county I live in, tobacco is commonly used and is a deep part of Kentucky's culture, especially in youth. Many of my peers use tobacco products, including chewing tobacco, and don't understand the risks. They participate in the use of tobacco because they think it will make them look cool. Some of the risks of chewing tobacco include addiction, cancer, and heart disease [4]. One way to help curb the use of chewing tobacco would be to offer programs in Appalachia that help current users quit tobacco. These programs could also provide education that would be aimed at preventing people from starting to use tobacco in the first place.

Throughout Appalachia, there are soaring cancer rates yet few treatment facilities. There should be more healthcare facilities so families who are experiencing cancer do not have to travel so far to receive proper care. For my family, my mother had to travel over 100 miles to receive treatments. People who are suffering from cancer should not have to be burdened with finding out where their treatment can be received. A solution to this problem would be to add healthcare facilities throughout Appalachia. This would provide access to treatments close to home for those who do not have the resources to travel. Cancer patients could spend less time traveling to receive treatment and more time with their loved ones.

Above all, programs like ACTION provide the best opportunities for young students like me to receive the training necessary to defeat cancer. The ACTION program is something I am extremely grateful to be a part of. Having seen cancer within my own family always made me strive to learn more about it, and now due to this program, I can. Programs including ACTION and those similar give my generation a better outlook on cancer and help us understand the science behind it. My group of peers and I within this program want to be the change. We wish to be able to help Kentucky with its cancer crisis. We want to be trained to fight this disease. Within this program, we are given opportunities to observe doctors and participate in cancer research. Being a part of this program has only driven me more to want to pursue a career in the medical field. I know my friends and I in this program can be the difference needed to make a change.

Cancer has been around for millennia, but I am not sure it has ever had a greater impact on public health than it has now. Currently, the Appalachian region is in a cancer crisis; this is likely due to a combination of factors including limited access to healthcare and high rates of tobacco use. The Appalachian region currently has one of the highest usage rates of tobacco. If there was a cancer education curriculum taught throughout schools, students might gain a better perception of cancer risk factors and students could gain an understanding of preventive measures. Cancer curriculum in schools will lead to the next generation becoming more cautious, ultimately decreasing the soaring cancer rates.

Kentucky's habits have to change in order to overcome the current cancer crisis. Every person has the chance to stand against cancer. The question is: will you take a stand and help reduce the high cancer rates in Kentucky?

REFERENCES

1. "Cancers Associated with Overweight and Obesity Make Up 40 Percent of Cancers Diagnosed in the United States, "Centers for Disease Control and Prevention, 2017, https://www.cdc.gov/media/releases/2017/p1003-vs-cancer-obesity.html.

2. "Adult Obesity Prevalence Maps," Centers for Disease Control and Prevention, 2021, https://www.cdc.gov/obesity/data/prevalence-maps.html.

3. "About Electronic Cigarettes (E-Cigarettes)," Centers for Disease Control and Prevention, 2021, https://www.cdc.gov/tobacco/basic_information/e-cigarettes/about-e-cigarettes.html.

4. "Smokeless Tobacco Products: Chewing Tobacco and Other Forms

of Smokeless Tobacco Are More Harmful and Addictive Than You Might Think," Mayo Clinic, 2021, https://www.mayoclinic. org/healthy-lifestyle/quit-smoking/in-depth/chewing-tobacco/art-20047428.

PRAYER REQUESTS

Alexandra Combs

Every Sunday, I sit in my family's pew at church and listen to the lineup of prayer requests and testimonies. I can trace some sort of connection to nearly everyone mentioned. That's one of the interesting parts of living in a small town: you know everyone in some shape, form, or fashion. You feel happy when the couple three rows back says their kid's surgery went according to plan. You may not know that person, but you've known their parents for longer than you can remember.

Do you want to know what one of the bad parts of living in a small town is? You know everyone. So, when the lady four rows up says that her mother was diagnosed with stage four lung cancer, the entire church, including yourself, feels horrible for her. She's been going to that church since long before you were even a thought. You don't even know what her mother's name is, but that doesn't matter. She's in pain, which means you're in pain. It doesn't matter because you know how that person must be feeling and are acutely aware that it could just as easily have been you in that situation. All Kentuckians have their own personal story, a story that has been shaped by high cancer rates in the state. These stories have led us all to conclusions on the causes of the high cancer rates and how best to deal with them. My story has led me through cancer, on a family and community level. That experience has brought me to believe that cancer is predominantly caused by smoking, poverty, and lack of cancer-based knowledge. I believe that Kentucky's cancer rates can be lowered by discouraging smoking, promoting public programs, and educating the public about cancer.

I'm from Wolfe County, which means I've lived in a very small town my entire life. We're just big enough to escape notice for being small and light-years away from being known as big-city material. When people find out that we don't even have a McDonald's, I can practically hear them begin to feel better about their own county's size. However, what Wolfe lacks in size, it makes up for in family spirit. If you were to take a drive with a longtime resident down the country roads that make up my town, you may be treated to a tour of the family "territories." You might be in for something along the lines of: "Right down that little holler are the Brewers, and the Smiths are all down this little road."

My family is lined up along Pine Ridge and Rogers Roads. We're a very close-knit group, being connected by more than just geography. We are united by love, friendship, faith, and, unfortunately, cancer. Sadly, various cases of cancer have afflicted my family over the years. My great-grandfather, Papaw Omer, passed away from brain cancer years before I was even born. Later, my great-grandmother, Mamaw Marie, got the horrible news that she had ovarian cancer. To everyone's relief, she recovered, but sadly was later revisited by the terrible disease and passed away when I was about 11 or 12. My great-aunt suffered from breast cancer, but thankfully recovered. David, my great-uncle, passed away from prostate cancer only a year and a half ago. My family was heartbroken when it happened. One of the main ways that cancer has wormed its way into my family was when my older sister contracted leukemia when she was only two years old. Thankfully, she recovered and has led a full, wonderful life ever since. Because of her close call, cancer has always been a very real issue to me. To make it even more prominent in the lives of my family and me, my grandma was diagnosed with cancer about a year ago. Despite growing up seeing and hearing about the effects of cancer, this was the first time in my life that I had witnessed the process and fully known the true terror of the situation. Thankfully, the cancer was in an early stage and she recovered, living happy and healthy today.

The reality of cancer always being in my life is one factor that led me to strive for a career among the people working to cure cancer. Seeing people inside and outside my family impacted by cancer gave me a keen sense of how much this issue needs to be addressed. The fact that I have always wanted to do something in the scientific field doesn't hurt matters. I have always been curious and loved learning; I was obsessed with National Geographic, adored anatomy models, and as a preteen, begged my sister for her college biology textbook. My love for science combined with a desire to help people and my understanding of cancer's threat led me to aspire to be a cancer researcher. I hope that someday I'll be one of those people working hard to try and cure cancer and help save the lives of those affected.

Despite my interest in science and medicine, growing up I never knew how much of an issue the cancer problem was. When I found out how bad cancer rates really are in Kentucky compared to the rest of America, I was spellbound. The state of Kentucky has the highest rates of cancer cases and cancer deaths in the country [1, 2]. I believe smoking is one of the main reasons Kentucky has such high rates. As of 2017, 24.6 percent of adults in Kentucky smoked, a higher percentage than the national average of 17.1 percent [3]. Despite how popular smoking is, it leaves a person vulnerable to all sorts of health risks, such as lung cancer, one of the deadliest types of cancer. When a person smokes, the poison in the cigarette can damage his or her DNA, causing a tumor. It can also damage the immune system and make it harder to kill the cancer cells [4]. More people smoking means more people are putting themselves at risk for cancer, no matter how healthy they otherwise live.

Another reason cancer rates are so bad in Kentucky is the poverty that ravages the state. Many Kentuckians, especially Appalachian residents, don't have the money to both pay bills and visit a doctor regularly. Instead of investing their money in screenings, they understandably choose to put food on the table. It's even worse for a person that has been diagnosed with cancer. Cancer treatment can be very expensive with the various doctor appointments and procedures that it involves. How can a person with financial difficulties possibly manage to pay the endless medical bills that come along with cancer? A lot of people faced with this potential problem choose to not even get cancer screenings, because they know they can't afford it and would rather live in the dark than in resigned fear.

Also, there are many people throughout Kentucky who are simply uneducated about cancer and the preventive services offered to them. How many people in their 20s truly know the danger that comes along with smoking? Do many 50-year-olds know how at risk they are and that they can get screenings for diseases like colon cancer for free? If people don't know the dangers of cancer and how easy it is to avoid it, it's not surprising that the rates are so high. Ignorance is one of humanity's greatest and most avoidable enemies. If a person is unaware that they shouldn't do something, they are much more likely to do it, and if that thing leads to something as serious as cancer, they are going to feel serious regret later. When people are uneducated about the risk of things such as smoking, drinking, and leading an unhealthy lifestyle, more people are likely to get cancer.

As with many things, discussing the reasons for the cancer crisis in Kentucky is a lot easier than addressing the solutions; however, if certain measures are taken, the Commonwealth of Kentucky and its inhabitants would be much better off in issues concerning their health. If Kentuckians were to make an effort to discourage smoking, promote beneficial programs, and educate the public, I believe the cancer rates would go down. First of all, I believe that an essential part in making cancer rates go down is to discourage smoking. One of the best ways to do that is to enforce the smoking age limit. The majority of smokers start during adolescence [5]. So if fewer teens were to smoke, there would be fewer people becoming addicted to smoking and putting themselves at risk for lung cancer. One of the best ways to curb underage smoking would be to punish the offender in some way. The most reasonable punishment would be a fine, similar to one a person might receive for speeding. If an underage person sees that there are consequences for smoking, beyond an hour of detention in school or being grounded for a week, they would be less inclined to do it. Another way to discourage both legal and underage smokers would be to educate them on the consequences that smoking has for both themselves and the people around them. If a person knew the danger that they were putting themselves and others in, if they knew how easy it was to protect themselves from one of the most common cancers, many would be discouraged from continuing to smoke, or, even better, from starting at all.

Another way to lower the cancer rates would be to publicize programs that benefit the community. Poverty is an immense obstacle to the people of Kentucky and it keeps them from being assured of their health. Public programs can either directly help by assisting with healthcare, or indirectly, by taking care of other matters and allowing people to have money to invest in their health. Both types of programs are extremely helpful and occur in abundance. However, a problem that many of these programs have encountered is that few people know the services that are available to them. How many people over the age of 50 do you believe would get a colon screening if they knew that the Kentucky Colon Cancer Screening Program [6] would pay for it, as long as they fit certain requirements? Just think how many low-income parents could rest easy at night knowing that the Kentucky Children's Health Insurance Program [7] is helping to keep their children safe. There are also many opportunities locally for people to get a little help. In nearly every county in Kentucky, there is a 4-H office striving to do right by the families in their county. Churches and schools are constantly hosting giveaways and fundraisers for those that need assistance.

Another obstacle for these programs, besides publicity, is the common idea that it is somehow embarrassing, shameful, or petty to use them. This is a myth that is as old as the hills and completely untrue. At some point in their lives, nearly everyone needs help in some way. However, despite how common it is to need help, people are often unwilling to admit it, afraid of being scorned or pitied. In these cases, people should know that if someone were to look down on them for their misfortunes, their opinion is not worth having. Another reason people might not seek these programs is because they do not want to admit to themselves that they need them, in much the same way that a potential cancer sufferer who cannot afford treatment would rather not know. As understandable as this feeling is, giving in to it does not solve the problem, only action does. Hard work paired with taking advantage of a program is the best and most pain-free method of escaping difficulties. On another note, many people fear using these programs because they do not want to wrongly take advantage of them. They fear that if they use this resource, there will be less to give to people who are truly struggling. I've faced times where I have almost let this feeling cheat me of a good opportunity. However, this is a very counterproductive attitude. If a person is fairly presented with a beneficial opportunity, they should take advantage of it. What good is a program if the people that it is offered to fail to use it? The answer of course, is none; so, to reap the innumerable benefits of these programs, people should step forward to take advantage of what is given to them.

Finally, a way to lower cancer rates is to educate the public about cancer and how they can protect themselves from it. Knowledge is power, and with this knowledge we could push back the number of cases and prevent cancer from destroying more people's lives. One way to spread this powerful knowledge is to bring it to the school systems. If a person is taught the right habits early on in life, they are more likely to keep them, as opposed to people who learn them later and are more set in their ways. However, there is a way that touches both groups. If children are educated about the threat of cancer and the decisions that can help to prevent it, they are more likely to shape their habits to match. Then the child goes home and tells their parents about it, and the parents are more likely to listen. It doesn't matter how many degrees a doctor or public speaker has, parents are much more likely to listen to their child who is begging them to stop smoking or to eat healthier. That said, facts and statistics from experts never hurt. While they lack the emotional tug that a pleading five-year-old has, data provides stone-cold facts and verification that cancer and cancer prevention is a serious issue.

The only people that can lower the cancer rates in Kentucky are the people of this state. Take this knowledge to heart and join the efforts to lower the cancer rates in our state. Everyone can help fight it, not just the hardworking doctors and researchers on the front lines of the battle against this disease. To truly beat this horrible illness, we need Kentuckians. Just by making a few smart decisions and putting forth a little bit of effort, you can prevent yourself and others from getting sick. By doing this, it is my hope that someday, while I'm sitting in my little pew on Sunday morning, I'll hear fewer people having to request prayer for loved ones facing cancer.

REFERENCES

1. "Stats of the States: Cancer Mortality," Centers for Disease Control and Prevention, accessed November 17, 2020, https://www.cdc.gov/nchs/pressroom/sosmap/cancer_mortality/cancer.htm.

2. "Cancer Statistics at a Glance," Centers for Disease Control and Prevention, 2021, https://www.cdc.gov/nchs/pressroom/sosmap/cancer_mortality/cancer.htm.

3. "Cigarette Use: Kentucky," Truth Initiative, 2021, https://truth-initiative.org/research-resources/smoking-region/tobacco-use-kentucky-2019.

4. "Smoking and Cancer," Centers for Disease Control and Prevention, 2021, https://www.cdc.gov/tobacco/campaign/tips/diseases/cancer.html.

5. "Youth and Tobacco Use," Centers for Disease Control and Prevention, 2021, https://www.cdc.gov/tobacco/data_statistics/fact_sheets/youth_data/tobacco_use/index.htm.

6. "Kentucky Colon Cancer Screening Program," National Colorectal Cancer Roundtable, 2021, https://nccrt.org/kentucky-colon-cancer-screening-program/.

7. "Kid's Health: Keeping Our Children Healthy," Kentucky.gov, 2020, https://kidshealth.ky.gov/Pages/index.aspx.

JUST A DISEASE?

Karlee Compton

Cancer means something different to everyone. For survivors, it can be empowering. For loved ones, it can be crippling. And for people who have never experienced it firsthand, it is just another disease that most people will not give a second thought. I have seen cancer destroy many families, including mine.

My name is Karlee Compton, and I am a freshman at Montgomery County High School. Cancer has impacted me more than it ever should have, considering I am only 14. My first encounter with cancer was when I was in the second grade. Until then, I had never thought about how deeply cancer affects people's lives. Because of my experiences, I would like to be an oncologic ophthalmologist, an eye surgeon that specializes in cancer.

It all started on what seemed like a normal day for your typical second grader: I woke up, got ready, then went downstairs for breakfast. When I arrived in the living room, I saw something I had never seen; my mother was crying. I thought, "What could be so awful that would cause my mom to cry?" It turned out she had just heard the news that one of her best friends, Joan Tackett, had been diagnosed with stage four lung cancer. My heart sank as I witnessed the sadness in my mother's eyes.

To my mother, Joan was like a best friend, mother, sister, and aunt, all rolled into one beautiful person. Joan and my mom would spend countless hours talking about politics and world events. Joan was several years older than my mom and therefore she had a big influence on her life from an early age. In my mother's eyes, Joan was perfect. The only thing they ever argued about was Joan's habit of smoking cigarettes.

Naturally, when I was born, Joan was a big part of my childhood. She was at the hospital when I was born. We shared a birthday. We always spent holidays with Joan and her family. She was a teacher, mother, grandmother, and a kind soul. Later in life, Joan became a high school history and government teacher. She had an amazing impact on her students' lives and on the lives of anyone around her.

Joan's cancer journey began one day in January of 2014. While she was at home, she suddenly became disoriented, with balance issues, and could not walk well. Her family decided to take her to the hospital. The doctors performed many tests. Finally, a doctor entered her room with some updated news. He coldly told her that she had stage four lung cancer that had already spread to her brain. Coupled with her family's shock, the rude tone the doctor used to break the news only added to the heartbreak. After just three months of fighting this awful disease, Joan passed away on April 1, 2014, one day after her 61st birthday.

My next encounter with cancer was five years later. In August of 2018, my maternal grandmother, whom I called Maw, was attending her great-grandson's birthday party. Due to the pain she had been experiencing in her hip, she fell while going up the stairs. Maw was taken to the emergency room and received stitches in her head and was treated for other minor injuries.

Several days later, she was still having pain in her hip. So she decided to follow up with her family doctor. The doctor ordered a computerized tomography (CT) scan to make sure she had not injured her hip. The results of the scan revealed she had two hairline fractures in her hip.

Several weeks later, the pain continued to grow worse. The doctor ordered more tests. Her doctor later discovered that she had some abnormal spots on her uterus. The next step in testing was a full-body positron emission tomography (PET) scan. This test revealed the devastating news that she had stage four lung cancer that had spread throughout her body.

Maw's treatment plan consisted of pain medication, steroids, and chemotherapy. After just one chemotherapy treatment, she had to be rushed to the emergency room. She was experiencing severe abdominal pain. The emergency room doctor found that she had diverticulosis. This is a condition in which small, bulging pouches develop in the digestive tract. The doctor told her it was not too serious and to watch her diet and stress levels—yes, he said stress levels. Imagine being told just days prior that you had stage four lung cancer only to be told a couple of days later to try and watch your stress levels.

The following week, Maw's pain had significantly increased, and she was transported by ambulance to the hospital. After another scan, they found that her diverticulosis had caused a large abscess on her colon and it had ruptured. They quickly moved her to a larger hospital for emergency surgery. After many hours of surgery, we were told that they had to remove part of her colon and that she would need a colostomy bag. The doctor was concerned about how well Maw would recover from the surgery due to the cancer diagnosis and treatments. This news was very upsetting for Maw because she had to watch her mother and two sisters go through the struggle of living with a colostomy bag.

She had helped take care of all three of them until they passed away. She did not want to put her children through that same experience.

She spent a couple of weeks in the ICU, and on Christmas Day of 2018 she was moved to a regular hospital room. I remember spending that Christmas with her in the hospital. Even though she was sick, she had planned to surprise my sister and me with a cruise to Aruba the following summer. We later found out that she had been secretly planning this trip for months now and she was going to go with us.

The doctors told us that her first and only chemo treatment had been what caused this diverticulitis. They also said that she was not healing very well from the surgery because the cancer had depleted her protein levels. Maw's body simply did not produce enough protein to heal her. Her oncologist suggested radiation therapy for the tumors on her spine to help with her mobility. She received ten radiation treatments while she was still in the hospital. Her team of doctors concluded that the treatments had not helped her cancer or her mobility. They decided to send her to a specialty facility that could help with rehabilitation and her other complicated medical issues.

Maw spent the entire month of January in the specialty facility. She never gave up hope and did anything possible to fight this disease. She trusted her doctors and did everything they told her to do. The doctors and nurses were in awe of her strength and determination in beating cancer. It was during this time I realized that she was losing her battle and was never going to get to go home. We tried to stay optimistic while around her, but we all knew she was getting worse and was never going to recover.

After just six months of fighting cancer, her doctors decided it was time to move her to a facility closer to home, in the care of hospice. On February 5, 2019, she arrived at the hospice facility.

She was able to speak very little but joked that the ambulance drivers did a really good job of transporting her. This was the last sentence she ever spoke. Her five children spent the next four days comforting her and reminiscing about childhood memories. On Saturday, February 9, Maw passed away at the age of 69.

I really miss my grandmother. I learned so much from her. I miss the camping trips, learning new recipes, learning about our family's history, and the best peanut butter fudge in the world. In honor of my grandmother, in June of 2019 my entire family went on the cruise to Aruba she had secretly planned for my sister and me. While there, we had saved some of the rose petals from her funeral service and threw them into the ocean as a memorial for her. When she planned this trip, she did not realize that she would not be able to go with us. So, by throwing the petals in the ocean, it felt like she was there with us.

My most recent experience with cancer was with my paternal grandmother, Mamaw. Less than a month prior to Maw's death, Mamaw was diagnosed with colon cancer. This diagnosis added to her already lengthy list of medical issues including diabetes, hypertension (high blood pressure), high cholesterol, thyroid problems, and heart issues.

As one might expect, colon cancer only complicated these medical issues. Mamaw had several tests done also. After a colonoscopy, the doctor said she had a tumor that needed attention as soon as possible. As a second opinion, she had a PET scan performed, revealing the cancerous tumor in her colon.

After consulting with the oncologists, she decided to have the cancer removed. The surgery was scheduled for April of 2019. Her surgery was postponed due to heart issues that would have complicated the surgery. The surgery was rescheduled almost a month later but was delayed again due to these same problems. A week later, she finally had colon cancer surgery.

Post-surgery, her doctors were confident that all the cancer had been removed. However, a few days before being released from the hospital, Mamaw suffered a stroke. Fortunately, after only a month in a rehabilitation facility, she drastically improved. Tasks like walking short distances, feeding, and dressing herself—tasks we take for granted—were slowly coming back to her.

Next, she was moved to an extended care facility closer to home for some extended rehab. About a week later, she suffered her second stroke. This stroke was more debilitating than the first because all the rehabilitation progress made thus far had been lost. This proved very devastating to her ability to fight and recover from the situation.

After two more minor strokes, the doctors told my family that the medication used to prevent these strokes and to thin her blood was causing brain bleeds. Without the medication, she would suffer additional strokes. At this point, the decision was made to discontinue the medication. Mamaw was sent home and placed in hospice care. After six weeks in hospice care, she passed away peacefully in her sleep on October 20, 2019, at the age of 74.

This loss was very devastating for me as well. Mamaw and I shared so many fun memories together. She taught me so many delicious recipes including cream candy, chocolate syrup, home-made suckers, and many more. I remember every summer, my sister, my cousin, and I would always go and spend the night with her, and it was so much fun. While she was sick, I would go and visit her every day possible. It was so devastating to see her get worse each time I saw her. It was absolutely heartbreaking to have to say goodbye to someone so special to me.

My experiences with cancer have forever impacted my life, and I no longer think of it as "just a disease." Cancer is a serious problem that we need to fix immediately. No one should have to go through all the pain my family and many others have endured.

"Lung cancer incidence and mortality rates in Kentucky greatly surpass those of other states and the nation as a whole. Not only is this one of the most common cancers, with 3,800 newly diagnosed cases per year in the Commonwealth, it is also one of the most fatal. And, unlike many other types of cancer, it is highly preventable, as about 90 percent are caused by cigarette smoking." [1]

As Kentuckians, it is imperative that we address this tragic issue affecting our loved ones. We need to ask ourselves how we got to this point and what we can do to help lower our cancer rates.

Personally, one way I would suggest helping decrease our cancer rates is educating Kentuckians on the harmful effects of tobacco usage. A common factor in all three of my cancer experiences is smoking. Joan, Maw, and Mamaw each began smoking before they understood the negative effects it has on your body. During their childhood, studies were just coming out linking smoking to cancer. However, since they had little access to the latest medical news, they—like most people their age—never realized tobacco's dangers.

"Tobacco smoking remains the leading cause of preventable death worldwide and is the single greatest risk factor for developing chronic diseases such as chronic obstructive pulmonary disease (COPD) and lung cancer." [2]

By educating people about the risks of tobacco and broadly spreading awareness, we can help lower Kentucky's smoking rates, which can lower our cancer rates.

Today, a common alternative to smoking is vaping. For my generation, this could be even more detrimental than smoking because we do not know the long-term effects this has on our body. I witness teens at school vaping in class daily. After school, you have to walk through the clouds of smoke just to walk to your car. Our generation should have learned from earlier generations that inhaling chemicals into your lungs is not good for your body. Unlike the previous generations, we should understand the dangers of inhaling these toxins. We have access to more medical information now than our grandparents' generation had; therefore, we should be more aware of the risk that comes with vaping or smoking.

As Kentuckians, we need to stand together to fix this issue. We can help educate young adults on the long-term effects of tobacco usage, vaping, and an unhealthy diet. If Joan and my grandmothers had been more educated on the effects of tobacco in their younger years, maybe their stories would have been different. We can also offer better screening options for early detection. If you detect cancer in its early stages, it might not spread throughout your body, and treatment options are much more successful. Once again, if Joan and my grandmothers had been screened earlier, their cancers could have been detected at much earlier stages and treatment could have been more successful. It is important that everyone receive their annual health screenings as issues can be revealed inside your body that you may not know are affecting your health, possibly in a devastating way.

While it may not be preventable, there are many things you can do to reduce the risk of developing cancer: healthy diets, regular exercise, abstaining from tobacco products, and yearly health screenings. Each of the ladies in this essay did some of the steps to improve their health as they aged. They also had regular visits to their doctors. However, it seems that many of their health issues were not reversible. In addition to blood screenings and other tests, physicians now recommend smokers have a yearly low-dose computerized tomography (CT) scan. Joan and my grandmothers were proactive in their healthcare as they aged. I have no doubt that if suggested by their physicians, they would have gotten yearly low-dose CT scans as recommended for smokers. Would these newer protocols have helped my loved ones? I can only think that it would have. It could have given me the opportunity to share another birthday with Joan, make another batch of cookies with Mamaw, and take the Aruba trip with Maw. By doing some of these simple things, we can help mitigate the Appalachian cancer crisis. It is my goal in life to help people in the same situations that my family has encountered. I encourage all Kentuckians to be proactive and take a stand to help get rid of this cruel disease.

REFERENCES

1. C. Hopenhayn, T. M. Jenkins, and J. Petrik, "The Burden of Lung Cancer in Kentucky," *Journal of the Kentucky Medical Association* 101, no. 1 (2003): 15–20.

2. H. Traboulsi et al., "Inhalation Toxicology of Vaping Products and Implications for Pulmonary Health," *International Journal of Molecular Sciences* 21, no. 10 (2020): 3495, https://www.mdpi.com/1422-0067/21/10/3495/htm.

THE CANCER CRISIS: WHAT CAN WE DO TO END THE TREND?

Isabella Dunn

"Optimism is the faith that leads to achievement. Nothing can be done without hope and confidence."

—Helen Keller

My name is Isabella Dunn. I reside in Magoffin County, in an extremely small town in the heart of Eastern Kentucky. I attend Magoffin County High School, where I am in the graduating class of 2024. When I was first introduced to the Appalachian Career Training in Oncology (ACTION) Program, I was in the eighth grade. Chris Prichard (the ACTION program coordinator) discussed with some of my fellow eighth-grade students and I the basics of the program and what it had to offer. I was very interested in the program, so I decided to apply. I truly thought that there was no way I could be accepted into such a rigorous, competitive program. Ever since I was little, I have always loved helping people and have always been fascinated with medicine-related topics. I would love to pursue a career in the medical field someday. This program has given me many opportunities that I would not be given anywhere else. I have a passion for assisting others and would love to make discoveries that will ultimately change healthcare in the place I love most. Yes, it will be difficult, but I have now realized that we can do things that are much more difficult than we could have ever imagined.

To me, cancer is the absolute worst disease to ever exist. Cancer can make a permanent impact on someone's life in just a short amount of time. Some people do not get very lucky when it comes to having cancer. To put cancer in a more exact definition, cancer is the name given to a collection of related diseases. In all types of cancer, some of the body's cells begin to divide without stopping and can spread into surrounding tissues. Cancer can start almost anywhere in the human body, which is made up of trillions of cells.

Normally, human cells grow and divide to form new cells as the body needs them. When cells grow old or become damaged, they die, and new cells take their place, but when this doesn't happen correctly, cancer develops [1]. Some may ask, "What is the leading cause of cancer?" The number one cause of cancer in the United States is smoking [2]. Cancer often has the ability to spread throughout your body, and it can happen very fast, sometimes without you even knowing it. Cancer is real. Cancer is scary, and it truly saddens me to think of the number of lives lost due to cancer each year. Cancer affects people of all ages, sizes, races, and ethnicities. According to the American Cancer Society, in 2021 there will be almost 1.9 million people diagnosed with cancer in the United States. And it is estimated that approximately 600,000 of those people will die. In Kentucky alone, it is estimated that 30,270 people will be diagnosed with some kind of cancer, and 10,090 people are expected to die [3]. So thousands of Kentucky citizens, and Americans, will get the heartbreaking news that they have cancer this year. Cancer in Kentucky is an especially severe crisis.

To me, knowing that we have incredible new technology and other resources to help us find a cure for cancer allows me to feel hopeful for the future. It is going to take the next generation of aspiring doctors, researchers, and other medical professionals to do incredible things for not only the state of Kentucky, but for the nation as a whole in relation to beating cancer. I believe we can and will do amazing things in terms of the advancement of medicine. We can all do amazing things for our fellow citizens. It takes true compassion and consideration, but it is worth it. Our people deserve the best healthcare possible, and it is very important that people can get the proper care for their health problems. Cancer is extremely hard to overcome, treat, and cope with. I truly believe that we can discover life-changing treatments that will ultimately change our lives for the better. As William Osler once said, "Medicine is a science of uncertainty and an art of probability."

Personally, cancer has impacted my family. There have been family members of mine on both my paternal and maternal sides who have developed cancer. Some of these family members are fortunate enough to still be here with my family and me today, while one person in particular was not so lucky. My maternal great-grandfather was in the United States Navy and was stationed in Guam. He only stayed there a little over a year because his mother needed him to help the family back home. When he returned home, he immediately went to work. He eventually got married and started a family in Indiana. Quite a few years passed and he and his wife decided to move to Kentucky to be closer to family. In Kentucky, he was always working to do his best to provide for his family. He raised four children, alongside his wife. He had nine grandchildren and 16 great-grandchildren (I am one of the 16 great-grandchildren). From what I remember and from what the rest of my family has told me, he was one of the funniest people to ever be. He had a great personality and loved making people laugh. However, he loved his family most of all, and unfortunately, he was diagnosed with prostate cancer in 1995. He lived with the disease for many years and did pretty good overall. His cancer later spread to his bones, and he did not survive much longer. In 2010, we had to say goodbye to our beloved papaw. He was a very special person to many different people and is missed terribly.

My other maternal great-grandfather also suffered from cancer. He served in the United States Air Force as a firefighter. He served there for four years. When he left the Air Force, he moved to Michigan and started a new career, working for the Goodyear tire company. He and his wife had two sons while in Michigan. After 15 years of working for Goodyear, he and his family moved back to Kentucky. When they arrived, they opened a country store in the small town of Royalton, Kentucky. They worked there for many years, and their six grandchildren practically grew up there. The entire community greatly appreciated the store and gave it great business. Besides working in his store, my great-grandfather had a hobby: fishing. Still to this day, he goes fishing whenever he gets the chance. He fishes many days of the week, if not every day, in the summer. It is very dangerous to be in the sun for long periods of time, especially if you do not use something to protect yourself from the UV rays. As unfortunate as it may seem, my great-grandfather usually never wore a hat, sunscreen, or any other type of protection from the harsh sun. Over the years, this caused him to develop skin cancer on his head. He seeks treatment for his skin cancer regularly and now takes the proper precautions necessary to stay safe. He still loves to fish, but he probably wishes that he would have used sun protection from the beginning so he would not have to deal with cancer now. It is devastating knowing that he could have protected his skin while doing something he loves so dearly. Luckily, he sought treatment early enough, so his condition was not life-threatening.

The final person in my family that has had cancer is my paternal grandmother. She has lived in Magoffin County her entire life and has also raised her son and daughter here. She is retired from the state of Kentucky and now enjoys her time at home. She is heavily involved within our community. She is a member of the Magoffin County Homemakers Association as well as a Masonic appendant body known as the Eastern Star. She likes cooking, doing crafts, reading, and spending time with family. Her children and grand-children mean everything to her, and we all appreciate her more than she could ever imagine. My grandmother was diagnosed with breast cancer in 2011. Her breast cancer was detected during an annual gynecological breast exam—not her annual mammogram. Following an ultrasound and biopsy, she underwent a lumpectomy and completed 26 rounds of radiation treatments. Since her diagnosis, she has faithfully followed up with annual mammograms and cancer screenings. I am very happy that she chooses to have regular screenings because it possibly saved her life. However, it is so sad to think of how my maternal great-grandfather could have possibly gotten the proper treatments necessary and could have possibly lived a longer life than he did. This is why I do, and always will, stress the importance of annual cancer screenings, especially for those who have family members who have suffered from any type of cancer.

As I am sure most people know, cancer rates are extremely high in the Appalachian region of Kentucky, and it is a normal thing to see people eating unhealthy, drinking, smoking, and using tobacco products. Our area is often stereotyped to do these kinds of harmful things. I believe that Eastern Kentucky has so much more to offer than just using tobacco or having high levels of cancer. You can easily link the high rates of cancer cases and deaths in Appalachia back to the extremely large population of people who abuse cancer-causing substances. People have normalized using tobacco and other harsh substances. However, I feel that so many people are just uneducated on how harmful their habits really are. If more people had at least some cancer education, we could decrease cancer-related deaths in Kentucky by a large number. This is why programs like ACTION are so important. Community outreach is essential if we want to take action over this terrible crisis. I feel that people are more likely to listen to an expert, rather than a friend or family member. Plus, if someone hears a child talking about the negative effects of cancer, they will probably want to see for themselves just exactly what they are talking about. According to the American Cancer Society, from 2015 to the present day, lung cancer has been in the top five most common cancer types in the nation, and it is the most common type of cancer in the state of Kentucky [3]. Yes, to tell someone to quit using tobacco is nearly impossible, but it is one thing we can do to end the trend. Educating and showing exactly how harmful substances in tobacco really are may just be the key to saving more Kentuckians' lives, and it would ultimately save more American lives. Another reason why the Appalachian region of Kentucky is so prone to cancer is because of poor diet. People are not receiving key nutrients in their diets. Many people are aware of the fact that eating unhealthy can cause a heart attack, diabetes, and high blood pressure, just to name a few. But most people are not aware that being obese will increase your chance of being diagnosed with cancer. If you gain a lot of weight, fat cells can very easily interfere and affect growth factors that can promote cancer [4]. Lastly, Kentuckians lack exercise. We have such beautiful mountains, trails, fitness centers, and many other places to get out and get active. We should take advantage of such amazing resources. Staying active will help you thrive during and after cancer as well as prevent it [5]. Exercise lowers your cancer risk in several ways. For example, exercise helps you maintain a healthy weight, whereas being overweight or obese raises your risk for several cancers. I believe that staying active is the best way to a happy and overall healthy life.

This generation of aspiring healthcare professionals needs to take a stand against the cancer crisis immediately. If not, there will be very serious consequences that many individuals will face. Since I have had to watch family members battle cancer, it is my priority to inform people about the harmful effects of cancer. My fellow ACTION students and I are very passionate about increasing our knowledge of cancer and ways to prevent it. It is not only the students that want this, but it is our mentors, the researchers, and doctors, all wanting to make a lasting impact on the people of Appalachia. Our generation is the future, and our future is looking very bright. This program has been a great eye-opener for all of us. Learning so many new things about cancer has truly changed my life for the better. I cannot stress how important it is that everyone takes our new discoveries, our research, and our opinions seriously, and I wish that everyone will apply them to their everyday lives so we can lower cancer rates in Kentucky. So, with that being said, I cannot wait to see what the future holds for myself and my fellow ACTION students. This is our time to help end the trend of tobacco usage and other harmful cancer risk behaviors in our communities.

REFERENCES

1. "What is Cancer?" National Cancer Institute, 2021, https://www.cancer.gov/about-cancer/understanding/what-is-cancer.

2. M. Fox, "Fresh Look at Cancer Shows Smoking, Obesity Top Causes," 2017, www.nbcnews.com/health/cancer/fresh-look-cancer-shows-smoking-obesity-top-causes-n822836.

3. "Cancer Statistics Center: Kentucky at a Glance," American Cancer Society, accessed 2021, https://cancerstatisticscenter.cancer.org/#!/state/Kentucky.

4. "Cancers Associated with Overweight and Obesity Make Up 40 Percent of Cancers Diagnosed in the United States," Centers for Disease Control and Prevention, accessed 2017, https://www.cdc.gov/media/releases/2017/p1003-vs-cancer-obesity.html.

5. "Your Secret Weapon during Cancer Treatment? Exercise!" Mayo Foundation for Medical Education and Research, 2019, www.mayoclinic.org/diseases-conditions/cancer/in-depth/secret-weapon-during-cancer-treatment-exercise/art-20457584.

TIME TO TAKE ACTION IN KENTUCKY

Emily Halcomb

Cancer. We all get that same gut-wrenching, nauseated, ominous feeling when we hear the word. It is an even worse feeling when we hear the word associated with a family member or friend who has been diagnosed with it. Our minds and bodies automatically go into doom-and-gloom mode since we know, all too well, how the story goes in Kentucky, especially Eastern Kentucky. Would you like to be part of the solution in the fight against cancer? Of course you do and so do I! Together, let's take action.

Hello. My name is Emily Elizabeth Halcomb. I am a sophomore at Letcher County Central High School in Whitesburg, Kentucky. My town is small, but the mountains are grand. I live at the foothills of Pine Mountain. I love nature and being outdoors, so naturally I love to hike! I am only about a 30-minute drive—and yes, that is a short drive for us around here—from my favorite place to hike at Pine Mountain State Resort Park. Lately, my family and I go every Saturday so that we can escape and meditate. There is just something so fulfilling and therapeutic about getting to breathe fresh mountain air, smell the flowers, hear the birds, see free-flowing water, feel the crunch of the leaves beneath your feet, and be able to share the most precious moments of your life with the most precious people in your world. These hikes have been instrumental in bringing my family together. I am so grateful for my family.

Family. This is something we all have in common, whether it be in Kentucky or anywhere in the world. We all have someone that we feel connected to that represents a sense of family in some capacity. It may be through blood relatives. It may be through adoption. It may be through friends. For me, family is the inspiration and motivation to be part of the solution in the fight against cancer in Kentucky, especially Eastern Kentucky. You see, four years ago, lung cancer took a very near and dear family member of mine. It was my grandmother, Edith Mae Eldridge. She was my best friend and pure sunshine in the lives of all who ever knew her.

Mamaw Edee, sometimes Mam, is what I called her, and she called me Em. Mamaw Edee took care of my brother and me as our parents worked. Her house was a second home to us. She always greeted us with hugs and smiles and we always left with hugs and smiles. Her religious faith was strong and her love for others was unconditional, especially for my brother and me! It did not matter what we got into or what we said, she never reacted in any other way than with love and kindness and positive redirection. She always had something good to eat and would often ask, "Did you get your belly full?" If not, you can bet she had more where that came from! Mamaw Edee was such a kind soul, always willing to help anyone she could! She had kind words for everyone and everything. She constantly encouraged my brother and me to stay in school to get an education. She always wanted to become a nurse herself, but never had the chance to because she married early like most people in this area did back then, started a family, and committed herself to taking care of her children and grandchildren. I feel like Mam's inability to fulfill her educational goals was the inspiration and passion behind her never-ending encouragement and support for her kids and grandkids to get an education. She always explained how getting an education would not only help improve the quality of our lives, but with it comes a responsibility to help improve the quality of the lives of others as well.

Improving the quality of the lives of others is why I want to become a radiologist. I have always been amazed by bones and the skeletal system of humans and animals. My goal is to be helpful and instrumental in assessing, diagnosing, and treating bone conditions and diseases. I never really thought of how cancer could affect bones until Mamaw Edee's cancer advanced.

At that point, I remember the family having worrisome conversations talking about how cancer has the ability to metastasize, or move to other parts of the body than where it originally started. Mamaw Edee's cancer metastasized to the brain and not the bone, but some people do have metastasis to the bone. In her honor, I have become extremely interested in cancer and cancer research.

Therefore, I am most grateful to be part of the Appalachian Career Training in Oncology (ACTION) Program through the University of Kentucky Markey Cancer Center. I feel like this opportunity will be more than just helpful to me on my journey to becoming the best radiologist I can be. It will help me learn how to identify the needs of others and take action to make a difference! I hope there is some way I can contribute to a cure for cancer! If not a cure then maybe I can be part of the solution in cancer prevention, more effective treatments, ways to relieve pain, ways to increase mobility, and ways to improve quality of life of those individuals affected and their families. If there would have been prevention, a better treatment, or a cure, then there is that possibility that Mam would still be here with us. Oh, what I would not give for another day to hold her hand, give her a hug, see her smile, and tell her how much she means to me. I would be quick to share how her imprint on me has made me a better person that wants to help and serve other people just like she always did, but in a different capacity as a radiologist. I think she would be pleased to know that I listened to her and that her legacy lives on through me by the actions I take each and every day!

As a radiologist, I want to know all about the bones, inside and out! I want to know about bone cancer so that I can provide the best quality of care and services to my patients and their families. I remember Mam would always ask her providers for the best doctor when being referred to specialists. She would just come out and say it: "I want one that knows what they are doing." "I want the best." And of course she wanted the best; who would not? Especially when your life is literally in the hands of the doctors with the treatments, or courses of action, they choose for you. I want to be that doctor my Mam would want to see and all other patients would want to see because they can trust me to always make it a priority to work at my best to deliver the highest quality of care to them and their families that I possibly can. On my journey to becoming a radiologist, I want to learn things like how does bone cancer start, how can we prevent it, how can we treat it, how can we cure it, how can we minimize the complications and manage the pain associated with it, how can we prevent it from metastasizing to somewhere else, how can we keep cancer that is somewhere else from metastasizing to the bone, etc.? My mind spins, races, wonders, ponders all these things that inspire me to study hard, to work hard, and to be committed to becoming a radiologist. The growing demand for doctors can inspire everyone. It inspires me to act.

Kentucky has high rates of cancer compared to all other states, with those rates being highest in Eastern Kentucky [1]. There are a multitude of factors that could play a role in why Kentucky, particularly Eastern Kentucky, is affected so harshly by cancer. Some people say the water that we drink and use has carcinogens in it from all the byproducts from coal mining and the coal mining industry, specific to Eastern Kentucky. Over the years, the coal industry has polluted the ground, water, and air. I have even heard some people say there is no telling what chemicals, byproducts, or contaminants have been poured into or disposed of in old, abandoned mines and into our rivers, creek beds, and streams. In addition to that, maybe it's the low education level of our Eastern Kentucky population. Back in the day, many people would quit school at an early age in order to go to work to help make a living to feed the family and pay the bills. Because of this, I think many people in the area are unaware of some cancer risk factors because they didn't learn about health issues. Low education levels also play a huge part in socioeconomic status because less education means lower-income jobs. So maybe it is the poor socioeconomic status of our region where people cannot afford healthy, nutritious foods that are rich in antioxidants that may help lower cancer risk. Healthy foods tend to be much more expensive to buy in the grocery store. Some people have gardens with a plethora of fresh vegetables come harvest time, but are they unaware of the harsh carcinogenic chemicals or fertilizers they may be using on their plants? Is the soil even a safe place to plant them in our geographical area? Is the lack of access to funds or transportation in general for travel back and forth to doctors' appointments a deterrent for people that causes them to put off health screenings? Or if someone is diagnosed with cancer, would the cost of cancer treatment be a roadblock for them being able to go places where advanced treatments or research exists, like Lexington, Louisville, or the Cleveland Clinic?

An observation of mine is that a lot of Eastern Kentuckians

use tobacco. It seems that I always see someone smoking or with a chew of tobacco in their mouth. Maybe the increased tobacco use is because we were at one time mass producers of tobacco for the tobacco industry and since it was bountiful and easy to access then people used it more frequently. In addition to the actual increased availability of tobacco, as I alluded to earlier, people are uneducated and unaware of the potential health risks to themselves and others when using these tobacco products. Science also tells us that genetics plays a part in cancer risk, as certain types of cancer tend to run or be more common in certain families. Is this because of something families are all being exposed to, because of a poor diet, not getting enough exercise, or is it just their DNA period that has a mutation that is passed through the generations? Who knows what the future may bring with DNA research? We may be able to alter DNA someday to take out the cancer risk parts. Attitude may be another factor. We may be predisposed to cancer through heredity, but our attitudes must be willing to change around the disease. Eastern Kentuckians need to become educated and motivated about their health. We must take action on the things that are within our control like diet, exercise, taking care of our mental health, self-exams, getting screenings, prompt follow-up with the doctor for early interventions, etc. To me, it is a combination of all these things together that became the collective reason why cancer so harshly impacts Kentuckians, particularly Eastern Kentuckians.

As far as what I think can be done to address cancer in Kentucky, I say it all starts with education. Education is vital. For one to act, we must know what action to take. This happens through education. For one to become committed to the action, they must know the benefits versus consequences of the action. This happens through education. If we did not know cutting back on calories, fat, or carbohydrate consumption and/or the increase of exercise to burn calories results in weight loss, then who would eliminate those things from their diet and/or exercise to lose weight? This happens through education. It is never too early to start educating on cancer prevention. Even preschoolers could follow along and understand if told about tobacco use in simple concrete terms and how it could cause sores in one's mouth that might turn "bad" and make you sick. As the child develops, I feel like the terminology should develop as well and more in-depth discussions should take place. In middle school they start sex education and start talking about sexually transmitted diseases. So why not have a cancer prevention class that talks about avoiding tanning beds, tobacco use, alcohol use, etc. This is just the tip of the iceberg as to what education could be provided and what education needs to be provided. Not only should these general prevention tips be shared, but educating people on how to properly dispose of things like batteries, oil from oil changes, and other pollutants is greatly needed in order to keep our soil and streams clean. This has to be done so that we can prevent toxic waste from seeping into soil and waterways. It is very important to teach about self-exams like skin inspections, self-breast exams, and self-testicular exams, and for one to report anything abnormal immediately to their doctor for an evaluation. It is very important to emphasize the timeliness of reporting abnormal findings, receiving an evaluation by the doctor, and early interventions that could reduce potential complications or even death. We should teach about getting screenings like mammograms, cervical exams/pap smears, and colonoscopies timely so that again if there is anything abnormal, it can be detected early and interventions put in place to reduce the likelihood of complications or dying. Once again this is about action. Taking action to educate our people.

We can do this! Let us come together with a commitment to service and excellence for educating our people in the fight against cancer in Kentucky, especially Eastern Kentucky, to lower cancer rates. Let's work together and build upon each other's ideas to make solutions around research, prevention, treatment, and a cure for cancer! Let's take action to improve Eastern Kentucky and the entire world!

REFERENCE

1. S. D. Rodriguez et al., "A Social-Ecological Review of Cancer Disparities in Kentucky," *Southern Medical Journal* 111, no. 4 (April 2018): 213–219, https://www.ncbi.nlm.nih.gov/pmc/articles/PMC5935122/.

A SIX-LETTER WORD

Gracie Harper

Cancer is a six-letter word that can strike fear, devastation, and grief into a person's life in a matter of seconds. Kentucky has the highest cancer incidence and mortality levels in the United States [1]. Cancer has taken over our Appalachian region and has left many devastated families behind in its wake. Finding a family that has not been affected by this terrible disease is extremely difficult.

My name is Gracie Harper, a native of Elliott County, Kentucky, and I am a freshman at Elliott County High School. For as long as I can remember, I have dreamed of becoming a veterinarian. Anyone who knows me would tell you that my love for animals is apparent. However, it wasn't until recently that I realized my love and fascination for a completely different occupational field: cancer research. Through the ACTION (Appalachian Career Training in Oncology) Program, a spark was ignited in me that has only continued to grow. Just the thought of contributing and giving back to my hometown, which has seen its fair share of cancer, gives me great joy. Although helping and caring for animals will always be something I enjoy, helping loved ones keep their family members around longer holds a much higher calling for me now.

Coming from a small town in Eastern Kentucky where

everyone knows everyone, I have seen that cancer cases affect us all and bring us closer when we hear the devastating news. Not only have people in my community been diagnosed with cancer, but people in my family have as well. These cases have put a huge hurt on all of us and changed the way we look at life. In the past, my neighbors and family members have had to say goodbye to a loved one who unfortunately lost their battle with cancer. However, thanks to the many advancements in the oncology field, many cancer patients are being treated and have been healed from cancer.

One of the leading types of cancer in Eastern Kentucky is lung cancer [2]. Many families in my community have had to deal with the devastating effects that lung cancer brings. I come from a divorced family. When I was five years old, my mom and biological father divorced and soon after, my mom remarried the man I refer to as "Poppa." Stepfamily is something that we don't recognize in our home, we are simply family and nothing less. My Poppa's mom, Judy, had already lost her battle with lung cancer when he came into my life. The story of her life and her battle with cancer is something that he quickly shared with us since it had such an impact on him. Judy was 56 when she was diagnosed with lung cancer that was not only in her lungs but had already spread to many of her other organs as well. By the time she realized she was even sick, it was much too late. Despite all of the medical attention and treatments, she lost her fight after only two short months. I could tell the grief and devastation that the loss of Poppa's mom left behind was still as apparent and ripe when he shared her story with me as it was the day it happened.

Poppa has always shared his memories of his mother's smile, her witty personality, her loving nature, her ability to always make the best of a bad situation, and her love for painting. I often wonder how different my life would be if she were still here with us. I am constantly reassured that she would have taken me in just like I was her very own grandchild. I only wish that I would have gotten the opportunity to witness the love she had to offer the world before cancer so tragically took her away.

Many other individuals in my community and even my family have also been diagnosed with breast cancer. Just last year, within the short period of a month, three separate women from three separate families all received a diagnosis of breast cancer. Instantly, I witnessed the people of our small town band together to fight the battle with them. Thousands of prayers went up, donations were made, and T-shirts were printed to show our support for these women. It was obvious that no one fights the dreaded battle alone. With the treatment given to them, I am glad to say that all three individuals are currently in remission!

Although breast cancer and lung cancer are both very common in the area, another type of cancer has begun to rear its ugly head. In just the last eight months, there have been three cases of leukemia in a neighboring county. Two young women that my mom works with were diagnosed and treated through a clinical trial. Young and vibrant women who had no other known health issues were forced to face a fight that neither of them ever expected. It is through treatments offered and the never-ending research to cure cancer that they both reached remission.

Now our community is banding together yet again to fight for and support the third victim that I personally know about who is suffering from leukemia. My friend's mother went in for routine blood work when she received a call from the doctor's office advising her to get to the ER for some follow-up tests. Scared and confused, she made her journey to the ER with her husband at her side. It was there that she was told the doctors expected leukemia due to the high white blood cell count apparent in her results. After several days of further testing, the doctors came to a definitive diagnosis of chronic lymphocytic leukemia. If there can be any good news surrounding cancer, this would be it, since her type of cancer is slow-progressing. Currently she is undergoing treatments and beginning the long battle of trying to beat this dreadful disease.

After observing my community recently, I have come to the conclusion that Kentucky is greatly affected by cancer. My realization comes, in part, from my lack of prior education concerning cancer. Before joining the ACTION Program, I had no idea that Eastern Kentucky has one of the highest cancer rates in the nation [2]. Before I knew this, I thought cancer was common everywhere else like it is here. After I told my family about this, they were shocked at how high the cancer rates were. Hearing this news really opened up my eyes and showed me how tragic this disease is in Appalachia.

I think lung cancer affects Kentuckians so badly because tobacco products are being used by teens in high school and adults everywhere. If I were to walk down the streets of my town, I could point out several people smoking either on the sidewalk or in their car. Teens are very impressionable and learn or do what their parents do. If a parent smokes around their child, then the child is desensitized and smoking is just a normal thing to them. If a parent was to never smoke around their child, then the child may be less likely to smoke. According to the Centers for Disease Control and Prevention (CDC), 29.7 percent of Kentucky high school students have reported currently using any tobacco products, and the CDC also states that 8.9 percent are currently smoking cigarettes [3]. Cigarette smoking is the leading cause of lung cancer [4]. Even if you don't smoke, exposure from the smoke of others increases your risk for cancer. This is called secondhand smoke, which can also cause lung cancer. The CDC article "Exposure to Secondhand Smoke among Nonsmokers" says:

"One in four nonsmokers, including 14 million children, were exposed to secondhand smoke during 2013–2014." [5]

Tobacco is so common in my hometown that each year we have a gathering called the Tobacco Festival. It is called this because tobacco is a huge part of our heritage. Coming from a rural community, growing tobacco used to be a huge part of a family's income.

Cancer is such a terrible disease and is an ongoing issue in all of Eastern Kentucky. In my opinion the lack of cancer education in Appalachia has a huge impact on why cancer is so prominent in this region. As I mentioned before, until I joined the ACTION Program I knew little to nothing about cancer and how to prevent it. I feel that youth need to be more educated about the cancer rates in the area and the causes. Now that I am aware of the risk factors, I am noticing residents of my town put themselves at risk every day. Teenagers and adults smoking and/or vaping, using smokeless tobacco, and using tanning beds are just a few of the things I witness from individuals in my community. Possibly people in the area are unknowingly putting themselves at risk due to lack of education around cancer risk factors, or perhaps they don't believe the risk factors to be true. I would like to see more literature on the topic of cancer cases in my area and meetings held to discuss and educate people on the topic. My hope is that by knowing the causes and risk factors surrounding the issue, individuals will become more aware and hopefully less prone to contracting the disease.

Families everywhere have been affected in some way or another by the devastating six-letter word called cancer, and I am quite certain that families will continue to be in the future if action is not taken. Just remember to take precautions, avoid risk factors, and help us fight this together. We must unite as one to battle cancer because no one deserves to ever fight it alone!

REFERENCES

1. R. L. Siegel et al., "Cancer Statistics, 2021," *CA: A Cancer Journal for Clinicians* 71, no. 1 (January–February 2021): 7–33, https://acsjournals.onlinelibrary.wiley.com/doi/10.3322/caac.21654.

2. T. Mandell, "Eastern Kentucky Has Some of the Nation's Highest Cancer Mortality Rates, Study Finds," Kentucky Health News, January 25, 2017, https://ci.uky.edu/kentuckyhealthnews/2017/01/25/eastern-kentucky-has-some-of-nations/.

3. "Extinguishing the Tobacco Epidemic in Kentucky," Centers for Disease Control and Prevention, 2021, https://www.cdc.gov/tobacco/about/osh/state-fact-sheets/kentucky/index.html.

4. "What Are the Risk Factors for Lung Cancer?" Centers for Disease Control and Prevention, 2020, www.cdc.gov/cancer/lung/basic_info/risk_factors.htm.

5. J. Tsai et al., "Exposure to Secondhand Smoke among Nonsmokers—United States, 1988–2014," *Morbidity and Mortality Weekly Report* 67, no. 48 (2018): 1342–1346, https://www.cdc.gov/mmwr/volumes/67/wr/mm6748a3.htm.

CANCER'S HOLD ON APPALACHIA

Nathan Hogg

My name is Nathan Hogg. I have lived in Appalachia my whole life, and I can't imagine growing up anywhere else. I am from Pikeville, Kentucky, but I currently live in Morehead. When I go to visit my grandparents in Pikeville, the number of buildings that are used for some form of cancer treatment blows my mind. The number of people affected by this terrible disease is shocking. Many people aren't aware of the risks associated with cancer, and common preventive measures are not widely discussed.

A few months ago, I had never seen the impact of cancer firsthand. I had never talked one-on-one with someone who has had their life torn apart due to cancer. This changed in February 2021 when I attended a Patient Advisory Group meeting with the University of Kentucky Markey Cancer Center where cancer patients, survivors, and their family members talk about their experiences and help one another with the struggles they're going through. I have never had a personal experience with cancer. Now, though, I have some idea of the effect it has on people. *Real* people. I've seen the faces behind the statistics. Even though I haven't had a direct experience with cancer, I can now see how impactful cancer is on people's lives. An estimated

10,090 people will die from cancer in Kentucky in 2021 [1]. That's 10,000 people who'll never see their families again. For a disease so widely researched and known, it takes too many people each year.

The people of Appalachia are a special group. They're the first to lend a helping hand and say a prayer for those in need, and they are some of the most resilient around. But, unfortunately, they're also some of the most likely to suffer the devastating effects of cancer. Cancer rates in this area are predominantly higher than those of the rest of the United States [2]. Many factors lead to this, such as lack of education, lack of affordable healthcare, and poverty.

There is a staunch lack of cancer education in our public schools. The only time I have learned anything about cancer is when reading the flyers at school about tobacco use. If we wish to decrease the cancer rates in Appalachia, we must educate the population about bad habits and poor choices that can stay with us for the rest of our lives. Cancer literacy, including being aware of risky activities and how to avoid them, is becoming more and more important. Informing the public about what behaviors lead to an increased risk of contracting cancer is vital in the fight to loosen cancer's hold on Appalachia. By doing so, the next generation of Appalachians will be well informed on cancer-causing activities and be better prepared to prevent cancer in themselves and their communities at large.

In many households, cancer is a taboo subject. This can be for many reasons, such as the loss of a loved one or simply avoiding the topic. In order to begin to understand this disease and lower the chances of developing it, we need to make it an open topic of discussion. With the help of people young and old, we can work together to increase the knowledge of cancer's devastating effects as well as preventive measures. Programs like the Appalachian

Career Training in Oncology (ACTION) Program are integral to increasing cancer literacy through outreach activities that focus on educating communities on prevention strategies. Educating the next generation is important in the fight to lower cancer rates, not only in Appalachia, but in the United States as a whole.

In order to even begin to quell the cancer epidemic in Appalachia, the healthcare access needs of the region need to be addressed. There are fewer medical practitioners per 100,000 residents in Appalachia than there are in the whole United States [3]. Combine this shocking fact with the amount of cancer in the region, and you have a recipe for disaster. With so many sick people, healthcare is imperative. Another healthcare-related problem is a lack of cancer screening in Appalachia. For many people, it is out of budget or completely unavailable.

The high poverty rates in Appalachia are another main contributor to cancer's impact on the region. Many residents of Appalachia were involved in the coal industry at some point. Now that the need for new coal mines is dwindling in Appalachia, due in part to a rise in renewable energy, many coal workers are out of work. In addition, many of these out-of-work miners suffer from some form of lung disease, several of which can lead to lung cancer. To top it all off, fewer Appalachians hold a college degree. This makes it difficult for out-of-work miners and unemployed Appalachians to rejoin the workforce without having to spend even more money on a degree. There needs to be a system to put unemployed Appalachians back into the workforce. This could be through cheap college or vocational classes or the emergence of new industries that can employ uneducated workers.

As you can see, there are several factors that increase the cancer risk rate in Appalachia, including a lack of education, lack of affordable and reliable healthcare, and poverty. These issues work together to make Appalachia one of the biggest hotspots for cancer in the United States. This is why, in order to make a lasting impact, we must educate the next generation of Appalachians, allowing us to ensure that the population is well informed on cancer-causing activities, and make certain that risk rates are lowered. Equity is possible in Appalachia, but there is a long hard road ahead of us. Remember, the change starts with you.

REFERENCES

1. "Cancer Statistics Center: Kentucky at a Glance," American Cancer Society, accessed 2021, https://cancerstatisticscenter.cancer.org/#!/state/Kentucky.

2. S. D. Rodriguez et al., "A Social-Ecological Review of Cancer Disparities in Kentucky," *Southern Medical Journal* 111, no. 4 (April 2018): 213–219, https://www.ncbi.nlm.nih.gov/pmc/articles/PMC5935122/.

3. "Getting Healthcare—and Getting to Healthcare—in the Appalachian Region," Appalachian Regional Commission, 2019, https://healthinappalachia.org/2019/06/19/getting-healthcare-and-getting-to-healthcare-in-the-appalachian-region/.

FIGHTING CANCER EVERY STEP OF THE WAY

Wyatt McCarty

Cancer, a six-letter word that turns our world upside down. Cancer is one of the scariest and most terrifying diseases that anybody could be diagnosed with. Many people don't understand how serious this disease is and how it affects so many people's lives. I have wanted to go into the medical field since I was a small child and I have read, heard, and even seen the effects of cancer throughout my journey in the 15 years I've been alive.

Hello, my name is Wyatt McCarty and I was born on June 24, 2005. I got accepted into the Appalachian Career Training in Oncology (ACTION) Program to learn about cancer and the ups and downs of it. Cancer is a huge problem in Eastern Kentucky today and this is how it affects my life, the hardships of cancer, and how it affects the world in many different ways.

I am a sophomore in Eastern Kentucky at Rowan County Senior High School and I have a dream of being part of something that will help people or save someone's life. My biggest dream is to be some type of surgeon and to try to save people from the things that might go wrong in their bodies. Saving someone's life or prolonging their life is my ultimate dream. Even as a young child, I was involved in activities to help promote health awareness. For example, I have attended an American Cancer Society (ACS) Relay for Life event with some of my friends to promote breast cancer awareness. Also, I remember selling a lot of pink lemonade to raise money to give to the ACS Cancer Awareness Program. One year when I was playing soccer in the fall season, organizers gave us the option to wear pink socks to promote breast cancer awareness and the whole team participated in the event. So I believe in educating people about the importance of understanding cancer and spreading cancer awareness to Eastern Kentucky.

My family has been affected by cancer. For example, my grandma has been diagnosed with melanoma and is currently being treated for the disease. Also, my great-grandma worked in a household cleaning factory and died at the age of 42 from cancer. My grandpa was married to a woman with one breast who consequently lost her other breast due to breast cancer.

A lot of people have known someone who has died of cancer. But what is cancer? Cancer is a disease. However, cancer can't be spotted and treated immediately like any other disease. This is because, well, cancer isn't just any other disease. It's a group of diseases that involve abnormal cell growth. Imagine being diagnosed with it and being told you only have so long to live. The day a cure is found will truly be a miracle, but until that day we must have faith and support different cancer research foundations in hope of finding a cure. Cancer means many things in many ways, but all people see cancer differently in their own ways. Cancer is a life-changing, life-altering, financially troubling, and sometimes fatal disease. It affects most families and almost every single human around us. Cancer is a very hard and challenging thing to overcome for everybody, especially in Eastern Kentucky.

The most common type of cancer in Eastern Kentucky is

lung cancer [1]. The reason lung cancer is so common in Eastern Kentucky is because of tobacco. Tobacco was a major crop for farmers in Kentucky for many years and became popular to the public. Eventually it became the new norm. It became so popular that kids started smoking it as well, but progressively tobacco became very addictive, and people didn't know that tobacco could lead to various health problems. One of the things that smoking tobacco led to the most was lung cancer. This is one of the main reasons why cancer is such a huge problem here in Eastern Kentucky.

I would really like to talk about how cancer indirectly affects me. My peers around me do not understand the consequences of their habits because they are slowly starting addictive, irresponsible behaviors that can cause cancer in the long run. Two of the most common behaviors are vaping and dipping. Many teens in our community today vape and dip, and it has become a major problem to society. People easily fall into these negative and addictive behaviors either by doing it too often or by being pressured by peers to start. The behaviors have various side effects, including leading to a variety of different types of cancer. Unfortunately, people don't listen to parents and educators about the dangers of these activities. Teens should be educated about the dangers of tobacco products and their potential for causing cancer. If teens would listen and not use tobacco or vape, the growth of cancer could slow dramatically.

Another thing that would slow cancer rates is if people used their five senses. First, taste: people could use taste to reduce their cancer risk by realizing that the taste of cigarettes is nasty. The things that might cause cancer the most are inhalants like cigarettes. Such products cause long-term effects such as throat cancer and mouth cancer. Also, in serious cases, mouth cancer can occur on the lips, gums, taste buds, inner lining of the cheeks, roof of the mouth, or on the floor of the mouth. All these cancers would affect a person's sense of taste. To go on, people might not know what taste has to do with cancer, but to their surprise, taste actually has a lot to do with it. For example, if you are diagnosed with cancer, foods may taste differently than before, especially bitter, sweet, and/or salty foods, and a lot of foods will taste really bland. However, some people who have cancer may taste all foods the same as they did before they were diagnosed. For the second sense, touch: if you smoke, you touch the cigarette to your mouth and teeth. In turn, your teeth can stain yellow and then eventually teeth can stain black, which will also lead to rotted teeth and unpleasant breath. So people can use touch to decide to avoid cancer-causing products. Concerning the third sense, smell, most inhalant products that cause cancer use smoke in the products, and to most people the smell of smoke is not a great smell. Use your sense of smell to avoid carcinogens. To go on, sight: if you think about it, sight can be used to slow the cause of cancer because people probably don't notice it, but many products sold today have labels on them that say that this could cause cancer, including certain household items. Also people see commercials about how smoking, juuling, dipping, and other addictive, dangerous products can cause different types of cancer. Although people see these things, many people ignore them because they smoke to either look cool in front of their friends or to help ease their stress from things that make them upset or aggravated. Last but not least, hearing. If you think about it, hearing can be used to slow the cause of cancer because people probably don't notice it, but many ads and commercials are put across various media platforms, and all people have to do is use hearing to notice the dangers of products like cigarettes. Overall, if something alerts our senses, then there is no reason for us to ignore the warning. Using our senses to avoid cancer is only common sense.

Not many people here in Eastern Kentucky are trying to come up with ways to slow the causes of cancer. Although a few people in other parts of the country and world have found and created different unique ways to stop it, we just have to find a way to put those great ideas to use here in Eastern Kentucky.

There are several other ways to slow or prevent cancer. The first is to never smoke tobacco. Using any type of tobacco puts you on a collision course with cancer. By now you probably know just how bad smoking is for your health and that it can cause cancer. However, it is not just smokers who are at risk. Tobacco smoke contains many chemicals that can cause cancer, and this puts both the smoker and people who inhale secondhand smoke at risk of developing deadly cancers. According to the Centers for Disease Control and Prevention, the cancers that smoking has been connected to include lung cancer, mouth, throat, larynx, pancreas, bladder, cervix, kidney, and several others [2]. Another way to prevent cancer is maintaining a healthy diet, which will help you avoid obesity. Obese people often have chronic low-level inflammation, which can, over time, lead to cancer. Sugar can be a cancer-causing food that you should try to avoid. Eating too much sugar has been linked to diabetes and weight gain, but those are not the only health risks that come with polishing off all those bags of sweets or drinking sodas, because cancer can also be the result [3, 4]. Third is processed meats. While hot dogs, bacon, and ham all taste great, they are not doing your health any favors. These processed meats are crammed with cancer-causing preservatives. Also, studies have found that red meat, even when unprocessed, is linked to certain types of cancer. Fourth is charred meat. Meats that have been charred or cooked over an open flame contain compounds that have been linked to cancer. Those dangerous chemicals are released when meats such as beef, poultry, and fish are cooked over an open flame or even pan-fried at high temperatures [5]. Although making healthy selections at the grocery store can't guarantee cancer prevention, it might reduce your cancer risk.

Next, I would like to acknowledge the importance of cancer screening tests. Screening can help doctors find and treat several types of cancer early, before they cause symptoms. Early detection is important because when abnormal tissue or cancer is found early, it may be easier to treat. By the time symptoms appear, cancer may have begun to spread and be harder to treat.

In conclusion, cancer is one of the most dangerous diseases known to mankind, which means that people need to be more open-minded about its causes and take preventive measures such as pre-screening periodically and learning to use their senses. There is a need for hope to cure the disease. We also need to remember to stay optimistic to convince and educate others that cancer can be beaten by people taking preventive measures and by doing research on the disease. Also, for people that are currently diagnosed with cancer, I encourage you to stay motivated and continue to fight it every step of the way. The human race does not need to take so many risks like smoking, vaping, and polluting their bodies with these harmful and cancer-causing products. Life is a precious gift, and you don't get a second chance. So what do you choose to do with it? The future of cancer prevention is not always up to doctors, nurses, or healthcare agents. Individuals need to realize that the choices that we make every day can increase the survival of this horrible disease. So my final message to you is stay strong, stay healthy, and stay cancer free.

REFERENCES

1. S. D. Rodriguez et al., "A Social-Ecological Review of Cancer Disparities in Kentucky," *Southern Medical Journal* 111, no. 4 (April 2018): 213–219, https://www.ncbi.nlm.nih.gov/pmc/articles/PMC5935122/.

2. "Cancers Linked to Tobacco Use Make Up 40 Percent of All Cancers Diagnosed in the United States," Centers for Disease Control and Prevention, accessed 2016, https://www.cdc.gov/media/releases/2016/p1110-vital-signs-cancer-tobacco.html.

3. H. Alexander, "5 Food Groups to Avoid If You Want to Lower Your Cancer Risk," University of Texas MD Anderson Cancer Center, December 2019, https://www.mdanderson.org/publications/focused-on-health/5-food-groups-to-avoid-to-lower-your-cancer-risk.h21-1592991.html.

4. D. Underferth, "How Does Obesity Cause Cancer?" University of Texas MD Anderson Cancer Center, accessed 2020, https://www.mdanderson.org/publications/focused-on-health/how-does-obesity-cause-cancer.h27Z1591413.html.

5. IARC Working Group on the Evaluation of Carcinogenic Risks to Humans, "Red Meat and Processed Meat," IARC Monographs, 2018, https://www.ncbi.nlm.nih.gov/books/NBK507971/pdf/Bookshelf_NBK507971.pdf.

CANCER IN MY OLD KENTUCKY HOME

Allisa Pack

I have lived in and seen quite a few countries in the world, but Eastern Kentucky will always hold a special place in my heart. This is where I have most of my family, friends, and where I feel at home, but my old Kentucky home is sick. My home is dying. Kentucky is plagued with a ruthless disease called cancer, and it takes root in my personal home too. According to the Centers for Disease Control and Prevention (CDC), Kentucky has the highest incidence and mortality rates for cancer in the country, and it's even worse in Eastern Kentucky [1, 2]. To the Appalachian people, this isn't just a statistic. It's the chance of their loved ones being taken and life as they know it changing forever. I am working with the Appalachian Career Training in Oncology (ACTION) Program at the University of Kentucky to help spread awareness and do my part to help the people's lives who have been touched by cancer.

I reside in Louisa, Kentucky, a small town in Lawrence County, a place that rests on the Kentucky-West Virginia state line. We only have about 2,000 people here, so everyone knows everyone. My family and I are the only Muslim family here, and I am the only Indonesian American girl around. Many people ask, "So why Kentucky?" My story begins with my father, who was born and raised here in the US and joined the military fresh out of high school, and my mother, who is from Indonesia and moved to the Middle East to start a new life. I was born in Doha, Qatar, a small country in the Middle East where my parents met. After a year of living there, we moved to Indonesia with my mother's family while my dad was sent to Iraq. After my visa was up, the best thing that was decided was to move to America with my father's side of the family. Now here I am, a sophomore at Lawrence County High School with a calling to help people in need. I have seen the sheer number of people in my community and in my family who have been impacted by cancer, and I want to help guide the people around me to a safer future. These are the stories of how cancer has touched my life and taken my family.

The first death I ever witnessed was when I was four years old. All of the family was sitting around my great-grandfather, sharing their favorite memories and saying their goodbyes. One of my aunts tried to give him his medication and when he didn't respond, the whole room fell silent. She lowered her head and fell to her knees, sobbing. Another relative rested her head on his chest to check for breathing. Tears streaming down her face, she raised her head and slowly shook it, telling us that he was gone. Even though I was very young, I felt that whole room go cold. I remember asking my mother where my father was, seeing him drop his head and leave shortly after, not wanting to scare me by crying. I had never seen my dad cry before, nor have I ever seen him cry again. Everything now is quite blurry, but the impact of seeing that as a child will never leave my side. I knew my great-grandfather was always weak, he could barely raise his arm to hug me back most of the time, but at the time I didn't know that he passed away from colon cancer.

Most recently, my great-grandmother passed away due to a stroke and was living with lung cancer. Like with her husband in the story above, I watched life slip from her as she took her last breath. Now, at 15 years old, I have more understanding of what it means to lose someone to cancer forever. In addition to losing the mother of this family, my cousin was involved in an accident on the way to the hospital. We thought we were losing two people in one day. Luckily, we discovered he only had a broken collarbone. That week was one of the hardest things our family has had to endure. My great-grandmother was the woman everyone looked up to. I can still hear her voice telling me "you're perfect" a few weeks before she passed away. She had never said that to anyone but me. My father bought us both matching birthstone jewelry one year since we were the only ones in my family born in August besides my grandfather. I now keep both sets of precious peridot rings in a box in my closet, away from the outside world.

One of the most important and influential people in my life, my grandmother, also had cancer. As I am writing this, she is in the hospital for a suspected stroke. Sitting in my first-period class and writing about all the ways I could lose her is something I never thought I would do. About three years ago, my parents drove us to Lexington. My brother and I were never told what was going on, although I had my suspicions. We drove to the Markey Cancer Center, where I was met with my whole family sitting anxiously in the waiting room. I later found out that she had ovarian cancer and was there for a total hysterectomy. About a year later, skin cancer was found on the bridge of her nose. They did a procedure to get out what they could, but her biggest fear is having some of the cancer left over and it traveling to her brain. She has witnessed the sufferings of far more people than I have and does not want the same fate for herself.

Countless friends of mine have their own stories and brushes with cancer. One of my friends I had in my accounting class last year just recently shaved his head to show his mom, a two-time breast cancer survivor, she is not alone. He tells me how emotional it has been watching the only person who took care of him nearly die before his own eyes and not being able to do anything about it. She has been incredibly strong and has kept her positive outlook on life despite everything that has been thrown her way. An old friend of mine found out he had stage four non-Hodgkin's lymphoma our eighth-grade year. None of our friends could believe that one of us would have this fate. Every now and then he would come back to school after treatments to attend a dance or have lunch with us when he was strong enough. Seeing one of the most bright, humorous, joyful kids I knew be in so much pain shocked me. Fortunately, he has recovered physically, but the emotional effects, I'm sure, will last forever. These stories, and many more, are the reason I want to help make a difference in my community.

Many factors go into why cancer is so prominent here in Kentucky. Lung and bronchus cancer is the most common type of cancer here [2-4]. The main reason for that is the smoking of tobacco. Many people are desensitized to the dangers of tobacco because it is a part of the culture here. Some people started very young and developed the habit of smoking. Younger people are always susceptible to peer pressure and are tempted by the promises of stress relief. E-cigarettes or vaping have become more popular because they are easier to hide and have flavors that appeal to younger consumers. There has also been the misconception that they are harmless, which in turn attracts more smokers, but this simply isn't true. Many people are gripped by harmful habits and exposure to smoking. In addition to tobacco, pneumoconiosis, or black lung, could also be a contributor to the massive amounts of lung cancer in my state [2, 4, 5]. Coal was the biggest industry in Kentucky until most mines closed in 2015 [6]. Thousands of families depended on the men and women who walked inside of a mountain by dawn or made their way underground every night. My family has a long line of coal miners who worked tirelessly in the ground, putting themselves in harm's way by inhaling coal dust for years on end. With the combination of mining and smoking, thousands of people in Kentucky find themselves struggling with lung cancer.

Poverty, healthcare, and education all go hand in hand when it comes to cancer. It is no coincidence that the states with higher poverty rates are the ones that are the least healthy and have the poorest healthcare and education. Rural areas lack access to good healthcare. Smaller hospitals in our area are understaffed, have shortages in funding, and are overall less equipped to handle more than the flu. The best place to turn when you have cancer is the Markey Cancer Center in Lexington. For people who live in my area, this is almost a three-hour drive. Travel alone can be very expensive, not to mention the cost of treatment. Most people in this area are already struggling with money due to poor education. Poorer children have a higher risk of dropping out of school because they are more likely to have to work to care for their families [7]. Dropping out of school lessens the chance of getting into college or receiving higher education, which reduces the opportunity for higher-paying jobs. This creates the cycle of not having the financial ability to afford better healthcare.

There are a few things that we can do as a community to prevent cancer in our loved ones and minimize the impact on our state. The first step in doing so is advocacy. Encouraging people to get screenings will increase awareness. Free screenings will make it more accessible to those who may not be able to afford it. Newer concerns have risen over the fear of going to a healthcare facility due to the possibility of contracting COVID-19. Appointments for screening for cancers of the cervix, colon, and breast were down between 86 percent and 94 percent in March of 2020 [8]. Making sure patients know clinics are clean and safe should be the number one priority.

To help with the strained healthcare system in rural areas, some local facilities may choose to join or affiliate themselves with larger healthcare networks to maintain or improve access in their communities. This benefits the smaller company by gaining the opportunity for better technology, staff recruitment, and group purchasing. Telehealth can also be a huge benefit to everyone. Patients now can see specialists in a timely manner while staying in the comfort of their own homes, cutting the costs of travel, childcare, and taking time off work. With the outbreak of COVID-19 and stay-at-home orders, as well as the advance in technology, more people in rural America are turning to telehealth for an easier, safer, and quicker way to stay in touch with their specialists.

There are measures we can take in our home and in our government to reduce the rates of lung cancer. Teaching children about the dangers of tobacco will help with the problem at its root. Setting a good example at home and establishing a smoke-free environment will restrict access to tobacco products. For those in the house who already smoke, many programs are available to help consumers quit the bad habit. This will also reduce the risk of secondhand smoke. On December 20, 2019, President Trump signed legislation amending the Federal Food, Drug, and Cosmetic Act and raising the federal minimum age for the sale of tobacco products from 18 to 21 years [9]. This will help discourage younger consumers from starting the habit of using tobacco. These are a few steps we can take to better our community and its health. The fight against cancer in our state starts in our home.

Cancer has established itself in my home in Appalachian Kentucky where it is not welcome. These stories I have shared and many others yet to be told are why I aspire to learn as much as I can and pursue a career in the medical field. With your influence on our family and friends, you can help prevent this deadly disease. When we work together as a community, we can be on our way to a happier, healthier future.

REFERENCES

1. "Cancer Mortality by State," Centers for Disease Control and Prevention, 2021, https://www.cdc.gov/nchs/pressroom/sosmap/cancer_mortality/cancer.htm.

2. S. D. Rodriguez et al., "A Social-Ecological Review of Cancer Disparities in Kentucky," *Southern Medical Journal* 111, no. 4 (April 2018): 213–219, https://www.ncbi.nlm.nih.gov/pmc/articles/PMC5935122/.

3. "Cancer Statistics Center: Kentucky at a Glance," American Cancer Society, accessed 2021, https://cancerstatisticscenter.cancer.org/#!/state/Kentucky.

4. "State of Lung Cancer 2020," American Lung Association, 2021, https://www.lung.org/research/state-of-lung-cancer/states/kentucky.

5. W. J. Christian et al., "Spatiotemporal Analysis of Lung Cancer Histological Types in Kentucky, 1995–2014," *Cancer Control* 26, no. 1 (2019): 1073274819845873, https://www.ncbi.nlm.nih.gov/pmc/articles/PMC6482657/.

6. "Business in the Bluegrass: Kentucky's Emerging Industries," Campbellsville University Online Programs, 2015, https://online.campbellsville.edu/business/kentucky-industry/.

7. K. Broadhurst, H. Patton, and C. May-Chahai, "Children Missing From School Systems: Exploring Divergent Patterns of Disengagement in the Narrative Accounts of Parents, Carers, Children and Young People," *British Journal of Sociology of Education* 26, no. 1 (2015): 105–119.

8. R. Robbins, "Routine Cancer Screenings Have Plummeted During the Pandemic, Medical Records Data Show," Stat: Health, May 4, 2020, https://www.statnews.com/2020/05/04/cancer-screenings-drop-coronavirus-pandemic-epic/.

9. "Tobacco 21," US Food & Drug Administration, 2021, https://www.fda.gov/tobacco-products/retail-sales-tobacco-products/tobacco-21.

HOPE FOR THE FUTURE

Matthew Sanders

I am from London in Laurel County, a beautiful town in Southern Kentucky. We have rolling hills with morning fog rising from them. The air is crisp and the water flows through babbling streams. Porches are filled with colorful flowers. A portrait of our community would be worthy to hang in a gallery. However, once the fog lifts, the sadness of the cancer epidemic is found lurking in our picturesque community. It is hard to believe that such a magnificent place could have such a high death rate from cancer. As a lifelong resident, it is sometimes hard to see the beauty of the area because of the hardships that occupy it. Many people want their children to leave and find a better life elsewhere, so their children do not have to face the same difficulties that they did.

People here are resilient, friendly, tough, and kind. They are always willing to help those in need to cook a big meal, to lend a helping hand, to start fundraisers, or to just sit and listen. They are proud people who love their families and their community. People often become preoccupied dealing with the care of others and do not focus as much on themselves. As a result, their health issues worsen, leading to complications with high death rates. Cancer, heart problems, black lung, obesity, and drug addiction contribute to a lower survival rate here compared to the rest of the country; life expectancy in Appalachia was 2.4 years below the national average from 2009–13 [1].

My maternal grandfather, Papaw, was said to be quiet, smart, compassionate, and a hard worker. He provided for and loved his family. He always helped others fix things in his garage at home—cars, lawnmowers, and anything else they needed help with. He also loved to read. He had a recliner next to his bookshelves lined with all types of books. If he did not know how to fix something, he would research it until he could figure it out. He also loved to study his family tree in his free time and enjoyed being outdoors.

Before he was married, he left the state to learn a trade, but the mountains he loved called him back home. He worked as a maintenance mechanic in the coal mines after he returned. He worked long hours and had to drive over an hour each way to get to and from work. He would come home and be covered in black coal dust and oil from the equipment. As soon as he arrived, he would have to clean up before he could spend time with his family. It is hard to visualize him being covered in that stuff for most of his day. It could not have been healthy.

Later in life, he was told he needed prostate surgery. His doctor did a precautionary biopsy which showed no cancer. After he did not get better from the surgery, he returned to the doctor, who did additional tests which showed widespread cancer. It had spread to several places, with masses in his bladder and kidneys. To get his chemotherapy, he had to drive to the next county, which was the closest location to his home. He knew he would likely get better care in Lexington, which was a couple of hours away, but he did not want to burden anyone to take him to his appointments. He was too weak to drive very far himself. He returned to his books to read as much as he could to learn about his cancer and tried to educate himself on treatments. He had other underlying conditions—heart disease, black lung, etc.—that worsened with the side effects of the chemotherapy. It seemed the treatment would improve one problem only to cause another issue to worsen.

I do not know if his occupation caused his cancer, but the doctors mentioned it as a likely possibility. Most people in our area believe that coal mines play a large part in the cancer crisis here, not only for the workers but for those living near the mines. It is believed that the mines left carcinogens in our water and our soil. Another belief is that surgery makes cancer spread. As with my grandpa's case, his biopsy showed no trace of cancer and the next time he was tested after his surgery, he had large masses. Since survival rates are low in the area, I believe that people do not want to fight cancer because they look at it as a death sentence. They have seen firsthand the pain and financial burden that it takes on families with many times the end result still being death.

Growing up without Papaw cost me a lot. I feel like he could have taught me about cars, we could have discussed books, and we could have spent lots of time hiking and exploring the outdoors. I remember in elementary school, each year they had grandparents' day. I know that he would have come every time and it makes me sad that we did not get to spend those days together. The same is true for all of my ball games and academic meets that I had growing up.

More recently, our family lost two neighbors to cancer. I can look out my door and see both of their homes. Their families have had to pick up the pieces and try to find a way to move on without their loved ones. Another one of my neighbors was diagnosed years ago and was able to beat his cancer. His doctors credited his good health as a factor in his success. He continues to lead an active lifestyle. He bikes, runs, hikes, canoes, and does just about anything outdoors that he can. I see him running by my house most days, and he continues to do it whether it rains or snows. He sets a great example of why it is important to stay in shape.

Being a part of the Appalachian Career Training in Oncology (ACTION) Program and studying the advancements of cancer care allows me to feel hopeful. I am not sure if a different treatment or facility would have saved my papaw, but I see the importance of providing good care closer to home and educating others.

Cancer is a terrible epidemic that plagues the entire nation, but its effects are not as evident anywhere else than in Appalachian Kentucky. In 2018, the state of Kentucky had the single highest cancer death rate of 181.6 deaths per 100,000 people [2]. Although it is surprising for most Kentuckians to learn, the numbers provide solid proof of how badly our state is impacted by this disease. The question is, therefore, not how bad cancer is in Kentucky, but why it is so lethal in our state. The high rates of cancer may be partially influenced by lifestyle choices, such as tobacco and drug use, careers in coal-related fields, and poor dieting and fitness choices leading to obesity.

A major component of the cancer problem in Kentucky is the frequent tobacco use among its citizens. On my daily route to school, I pass multiple discount tobacco stands. It is extremely rare to take a trip to a public place like the supermarket or a restaurant without encountering someone smoking a cigarette. Based on a study by the CDC, Kentucky has the second-highest percentage of current cigarette use among adults of any state, only behind West Virginia [3]. As tobacco is a widely known carcinogen, this frequent use of tobacco has to be a significant contributor to the high cancer rates. The scary part, however, is not just the risk to the lifelong smokers in the area but also the risk to the new generation of tobacco users. In this area, it is not uncommon for some teenagers to start smoking cigarettes or using chewing tobacco. Now there is a new threat with the creation of e-cigarettes. Over the past few years, "vaping" has become a popular trend among teenagers around the country, including in our home counties. Even with limited datasets, studies have shown that there are dangerous carcinogens within these products; furthermore, e-cigarettes have been considered a gateway drug into the use of tobacco [4]. In order to combat tobacco and e-cigarette use, Kentucky has raised the age required to purchase tobacco products as well as instituting a higher tobacco tax throughout the state to discourage its use [5].

The countless years spent in the coal industry are definitely a contributor to cancer in Kentucky and Appalachia. Based on one study, coal miners had a significantly higher risk of any cancer, and those with over 15 years of experience had a significantly higher risk of lung cancer [6]. Coal dust is breathed into the lungs of these workers, inhibiting cellular function and causing cancer. However, it is a common belief in this area that substances from the coal mines across the state have seeped into various waterways, causing the general public to ingest carcinogens. This theoretically leads to a widespread presence of cancers other than lung cancer throughout our community. Although there have been few studies conducted in Appalachian Kentucky to support this, these claims could be proven with evidence from more research. To fight this, the community needs to create jobs for coal miners in other industries, allowing for safer working conditions. On top of this, there need to be stronger regulations on abandoned coal mines in order to keep any carcinogenic chemicals inside the mines and outside our communities. There is also a great need for intense studies in this area to find ways to lessen the effects of any harmful chemicals that are already present within our environment.

Laurel County, like many other counties in the Appalachian area, is plagued with poverty. According to census data, in 2018 Kentucky's median household income was a little over $54,000, which was almost $10,000 less than the national median of around $63,000 [7]. Furthermore, another study stated that the per capita average income in Appalachia in 2015 was $38,593, which was significantly lower than the national average of $48,112 [8]. Poverty can increase the risks of fatality from cancer in many ways. First off, many people cannot or feel that they cannot afford treatments, so they do not attempt to get them. If they do seek help, they tend to stay within their local communities where there is a lack of specialized doctors rather than going somewhere like Lexington where there are more specialists. This is related to a mentality commonly referred to as fatalism, in which people will simply not get treatments, as they feel they will die either way, so it is not worth wasting their family's money. Poverty can also lead people to make poor lifestyle choices. For example, people will be more inclined to eat daily from a fast-food restaurant rather than to spend more money on healthier alternatives. Food stamps also will pay for more junk food compared to healthier but more expensive options like fresh produce. To address the effects of poverty in Kentucky, the government could raise the state minimum wage or allow food stamps to contain benefits that encourage people to buy more fresh produce at a reduced cost. To address the fatalism mentality, we need to ensure that people realize the importance of getting good treatments as well as finding methods of making treatments more accessible and more affordable. Also, current students of Appalachia need to realize the lack of medical professionals in their home counties and be willing to fill the void as adults. In other words, youth from Appalachia need to undergo the training to become medical specialists so that they can come back to the area and serve their communities. With more professionals across the state, cancer patients would not have to face the burden of travel that hinders so many from specialized treatment.

Another important factor in fighting cancer in Kentucky is education. Everyone in the area has heard of cancer and its destructive effects, but few actually know much about it, such as what it is, or more importantly, that it is preventable and curable. For instance, lung cancer, the most prevalent cancer in Kentucky, could likely be reduced if cautions against the practices mentioned earlier—like smoking—were taken. Kentuckians can be helped in the battle against cancer by educational programs such as the Kentucky Tobacco Prevention and Cessation Program. This is a federally funded program that provides free resources to people in our state who want to quit their tobacco use [9]. If more people took advantage of programs such as this one, then tobacco usage rates could fall dramatically, and hopefully cancer rates in the area would follow. A more effective approach, however, is not through cessation programs but through educational programs that discourage people from starting deadly habits in the first place. Along with these precautions, more awareness is needed on the power of screenings. By getting screenings, cancers can be detected in a much earlier stage, making the possibility of successful treatment much higher.

In the progression for development of future treatments, it is important that people know exactly what cancer is. Unlike a traditional infection, which is caused by an invasive agent, cancer itself is caused by a genetic mutation that allows the cell to multiply uncontrollably. This causes overcrowding as well as not allowing the cells to perform their specific functions. More specifically, studies have shown that most of these cancer-causing mutations occur in the p53 gene or genes directly related to the p53 gene [10]. The p53 gene (nicknamed the "Guardian of the Genome") is a tumor-suppression gene that regulates the cell cycle. In order to find more effective cancer treatments, research could be focused on the functions of this gene and causes for its mutations; theoretically, if methods could be found to prevent or even reverse these mutations, then a much higher survival rate could be achieved.

Technology will be instrumental in the ongoing research for improved cancer treatments such as mutations related to the p53 gene. Artificial intelligence (AI) is the term where a computer is programmed to learn and reason similarly to humans. AI excels at recognizing patterns in large volumes of data that cannot be perceived by the human brain. Integration of AI technology in cancer care could improve the accuracy and speed of diagnoses, aid clinical decision-making, and lead to better health outcomes [11]. Another recent tool that is being utilized in cancer research is called CRISPR (clustered regularly interspaced short palindromic repeats). CRISPR is a gene-editing tool that could allow mutations in DNA to be cut out and replaced with normal sequences. "CRISPR is becoming a mainstream methodology used in many cancer biology studies because of the convenience of the technique," said Jerry Li, MD, PhD, of the National Cancer Institute's Division of Cancer Biology [12]. When used together, tools such as AI and CRISPR may be able to better identify DNA mutations in cancer patients and cut out and replace them with healthy DNA sequences. Tools such as these are still in a developmental stage, but they do show promising results for the future. If developed technology could be adopted into treatments in Appalachian Kentucky, it might be possible to keep the communities traditionally ruptured by the cancer epidemic intact. People of Appalachia may initially be reluctant to consider new treatments such as gene editing, but they would be more than eager to adopt new methods once the technology has been proven effective in fighting cancer.

Where I come from, it is extremely rare to find someone who has not had either a family member or friend affected by cancer. Cancer devastates not only the life of the patient but the entire community that supports them. With more education for preventive measures and continued extensive research, maybe the cancer death rates would drop significantly, keeping our communities whole. This way, future generations might have an opportunity to get to know their grandparents, an opportunity that I did not have. This gives me hope for the future.

REFERENCES

1. G. K. Singh, M. D. Kogan, and R. T. Slifkin, "Widening Disparities In Infant Mortality and Life Expectancy between Appalachia and the Rest of the United States, 1990–2013," *Health Affairs* 36, no. 8 (2017): 1423–1432, https://www.healthaffairs.org/doi/10.1377/hlthaff.2016.1571.

2. "Cancer Mortality by State," Centers for Disease Control and Prevention, 2021, https://www.cdc.gov/nchs/pressroom/sosmap/cancer_mortality/cancer.htm.

3. "Map of Current Cigarette Use among Adults," Centers for Disease Control and Prevention, 2018, https://www.cdc.gov/statesystem/cigaretteuseadult.html.

4. S. Chapman, D. Bareham, and W. Maziak, "The Gateway Effect of E-Cigarettes: Reflections on Main Criticisms," *Nicotine & Tobacco Research* 21, no. 5 (2019): 695–698, https://www.ncbi.nlm.nih.gov/pmc/articles/PMC6468127/.

5. J. Cheves, "Kentucky House Panel Approves $50 Million Tax Increase on Vaping, Other Tobacco Products," *Lexington Herald-Leader*, February 11, 2020, https://www.kentucky.com/news/politics-government/article240185867.html.

6. W. D. Jenkins et al., "Population Cancer Risks Associated with Coal Mining: a Systematic Review," *PLoS One* 8, no. 8 (2013): e71312, https://www.ncbi.nlm.nih.gov/pmc/articles/PMC3744577/.

7. "Table H-8: Median Household Income by State: 1984 to 2018," US Census Bureau, 2018, https://www2.census.gov/programs-surveys/cps/tables/time-series/historical-income-households/h08.xls.

8. "Relative Per Capita Income Rates in Appalachia, 2015," Appalachian Regional Commission, 2015, https://www.arc.gov/map/relative-per-capita-income-rates-in-appalachia-2015/.

9. "Tobacco Prevention and Cessation Program," Kentucky Cabinet for Health and Family Services, 2017, https://chfs.ky.gov/agencies/dph/dpqi/cdpb/Pages/tobcessation.aspx.

10. V. P. Almazov, D. V. Kochetkov, and P. M. Chumakov, "The Use of p53 as a Tool for Human Cancer Therapy," *Molecular Biology (Mosk)* 41, no. 6 (2007): 947–963, https://www.ncbi.nlm.nih.gov/pmc/articles/PMC2634859/.

11. "Artificial Intelligence: Opportunities in Cancer Research," National Cancer Institute, 2020, https://www.cancer.gov/research/areas/diagnosis/artificial-intelligence.

12. "How CRISPR Is Changing Cancer Research and Treatment," National Cancer Institute, 2020, https://www.cancer.gov/news-events/cancer-currents-blog/2020/crispr-cancer-research-treatment.

CANCER: EVEN IF YOU SEE IT COMING, YOU NEVER EXPECT IT

John Staton

Family is a word with many dictionary definitions and many social forms, but only one description holds true meaning . . . the group of people you hold closest in your heart. These are your real forever supporters; the ones who will always love you and will always have your back. In my family, we are raised to be a positive influence on each other; to be each other's greatest critics while also loving each other unconditionally. There is no situation where we do not support, assist, or show endearment toward each other, even in the hardest times. My family are the people who walked together and supported each other during the stories I am about to tell.

I am John Staton, but most of my friends call me JT. I am from a very scaled-down, laid-back town in Carter County, located in Eastern Kentucky. My town embodies the old cliché that everybody knows everybody, and everyone calls you a friend. There is a quite simple way of living in a small town, where everyone you meet is an influence on your life, and many play an intricate part. I am currently a freshman at Elliott County High School. I am full of hope and ambition and a desire to contribute something positive to the people and region I love. This was my inspiration for applying to the Appalachian Career Training in Oncology (ACTION) Program, to lay the groundwork for further opportunities beyond my small town.

Coming from a small place like Carter County, it is easy to see the contrasting ways of life in the area. On the same streets, you will see people driving upscale cars and people walking because they have no car. You will see people living in upscale homes often next door to small, run-down homes. However, I was taught not to judge people by their economic conditions, and I do not care how much money someone has. Guess what? Cancer does not care either! From the richest of the rich to the poorest of the poor, from celebrities like Alex Trebek to anonymous people in Appalachian Kentucky, all are subject to cancer.

Many of the people I encounter daily have had some form of cancer experience in their lives, either personally or through family and friends. Cancer is like a storm cloud hanging over humanity. Once you have experienced its wrath, it casts a shadow on life, and you always fear the next potential storm. You will value life in an entirely different way.

I am the grandson of a cancer survivor. I am also the nephew, great-great-nephew, and grandson of three amazing people who lost their battles with cancer. The following are their stories and how their cancer journeys affected my life.

MY PATERNAL GRANDFATHER

My most recent dealing with cancer was with my paternal grandfather, John Staton Sr., who, in 2018 at the age of 75, was diagnosed with the most common type of skin cancer. Until that time he had been a healthy man. The first sign of illness was one small blemish appearing directly behind his right earlobe. Being a Vietnam veteran with medical benefits from his service, he sought care through the VA healthcare system. His medical provider, a dermatologist, ordered various tests and samples collected to assess his situation. After a long, stressful waiting period, my family received results we never expected—my grandfather was diagnosed with early-stage basal cell carcinoma. Based on this result, the dermatologist referred him to a surgical oncologist for treatment.

For as long as I can remember, my grandfather was independent and stubborn, with extremely strict, faith-based beliefs. Upon learning his diagnosis, this disposition led him to initially reject any sort of treatment, even at the urging of family. Rather, he insisted on just living with the cancer and treating it with his "home remedies." Although the family was not surprised with his decision, as a 12-year-old child, it was difficult for me to process. He fully resisted going to any more doctors; he declined any medication; he refused further testing; and he most certainly objected to an operation. Not surprisingly, his health began to decline rapidly. He lost weight and his physical strength decreased, all while the cancerous blemish was enlarging.

Faced with the overall decrease in his health, my grandpa finally dealt with the reality of what was happening to him and scheduled a follow-up appointment. The dermatologist immediately renewed a referral to a surgical oncologist and demanded a rushed appointment date. At that oncology appointment he was advised that he would need an operation to remove the cancerous skin and tissue. Three weeks later he underwent the operation, which was a surprisingly short procedure that successfully removed the cancer. Though the recovery time was long and sometimes difficult, he was a survivor . . . and that was what mattered most to my family.

MY GREAT-GREAT-AUNT

Although I was not directly involved in this particular cancer battle, it greatly affected me through the deep impact it had on my family. My great-great-aunt, Patty, passed with cancer in December 2014. Her story spans three decades of intermittent cancer, interspersed with years of seemingly good health and a happy life.

I have heard so many stories about this sweet lady, her well-lived life, and her cancer ordeal. She was a strong, well-respected woman who was the true definition of a warrior. Her battle with cancer began in 1985, 21 years before I was born. Her initial diagnosis was breast cancer, confined to the left breast, which required a single mastectomy. After this successful surgery, she became a long-term survivor. However, in 2010, she began having pulsating back pain for which she made an appointment with her primary care provider. Her physician initially believed the back pain to be pain from preexisting knee issues. She eventually sought pain care through a chiropractor. After performing the routine, pretreatment X-rays of her back, the chiropractor saw something of concern. Rather than receiving chiropractic care, Patty was immediately scheduled to have a CT scan later that same day. What the chiropractor had seen on the X-ray was revealed in greater detail on the CT scan: a large mass on the spine. She was then referred back to her primary care provider, who made further referral to the hospital for a biopsy. The biopsy results were heartbreaking for my family; there was active cancer that had created a hole in her spine.

The oncologist made immediate plans for treatment. Initially Patty underwent numerous amounts of radiation treatment; then she began receiving chemo. Because the cancer had destabilized her spine, she was advised to limit walking, bending, and other routines of daily life. Aunt Patty had always been an outgoing, active person, but this disease restricted her from enjoying her usual activities.

After doing months of this treatment regimen, she noticed a large, fluid-filled knot on the upper back side of her shoulder. At her regularly scheduled oncology appointment, it was decided to drain the fluid from the knot and biopsy it as a precaution. The results revealed an even worse scenario—the breast cancer had returned. As a result, she was administered stronger treatments at more frequent intervals. At this point, doctors advised her that she would never again be cancer free and that she would have to undergo extreme treatment for the rest of her life. She even entered an experimental chemo program.

Yet there was more to come. Patty began having trouble breathing. As a routine precaution, the doctor did a chest X-ray. A mass was discovered in her lung. She was immediately admitted into the hospital, where a rapid-result biopsy revealed the breast cancer had spread to her lung. Shortly afterwards, her health began declining rapidly. A full-body scan revealed cancer in her brain. At this point, my family had to hear the worst possible news . . . there was nothing else to be done. Patty was placed under hospice care at home, where she remained for six weeks. She passed on December 7, 2014.

"For she didn't lose the battle, she fought till the very end."
—I Timothy 6:12

MY AUNT

Watching my aunt, Amanda Binion, fight a losing battle with ovarian cancer was a heartbreaking journey, and I will always hold her near and dear in my heart. Her ordeal began in 2013 when she was admitted into the hospital with severe abdominal pain. Multiple tests were conducted, including ultrasounds and CT scans. The only finding was a large pocket of fluid in the abdominal area, which doctors assessed could be surgically removed. The operation was conducted the next day. The surgeon indicated that the fluid was nothing of concern, and no rush was put on the lab assessment. However, three days later a devastating diagnosis was delivered—stage four ovarian cancer.

At that point, it was decided that her treatment and care plan would be handled by the Markey Cancer Center in Lexington, Kentucky. Her case was given priority and an appointment was scheduled for just a few days later. At that first assessment, the oncology team reviewed her pathology report and decided on the first treatment step; she would need a complete hysterectomy. The surgery was scheduled for a few weeks later. Those weeks were filled with anxious waiting and nervous anticipation of my family. When the day arrived, we were prepared for a relatively simple procedure, which ultimately turned into a grueling operation. In addition to the typical hysterectomy, it was necessary to remove most of the omentum (the covering for vital organs and intestines). After completion of the surgery, she remained in the UK hospital for around one week. Upon her release, she had little time to rest before the chemo began. She then faced increasing strain from various medical issues such as bowel blockages, all complications from the cancer. In a short while her chemo treatment was changed, as repetitive testing showed the current type of infusion was not working for her cancer. After beginning the new chemo, she began having issues with pain and not being able to flush her kidneys. Diagnostic testing revealed permanent damage to the kidneys due to the repetitive rounds of chemo. Referral was then made to a nephrologist, and she began dialysis. She continued receiving chemo treatments once a month while doing dialysis three days a week as well as routine testing and checkups. Although she fought hard, her life being consumed with this regimented schedule, she lost her battle with cancer on July 16, 2015.

> "Cancer lost the battle against you because it inadvertently made you stronger."
>
> —unknown

MY MATERNAL GRANDFATHER

This particular battle is especially memorable for me because I was very directly involved. My papaw, Terry Maggard, was probably my closest and most difficult cancer experience. This man was not only my maternal grandfather but my best friend. Some of my best memories as a child are with him. I was his only grandson and, typically, I refused to leave his side the majority of the time because he was such a part of me. We had a special, close grandpa/grandson relationship . . . as I would have swum across the ocean for him as he would have for me. Our relationship became even closer once he became ill from esophageal cancer.

In 2010, my papaw became extremely ill. His health decreased rapidly as he lost weight, lost his appetite, and lost much of his enthusiasm. His primary healthcare provider was uncertain what was going on, so she referred him to a gastroenterologist to identify the issue. After being seen by the specialist, a colonoscopy and an endoscopy were ordered. These tests identified a small, unusual spot on the interior of his esophagus. At the time, this was believed to be nothing other than irritation from Barrett's esophagus, produced by gastroesophageal reflux disease. However, the doctor decided to biopsy a small segment of the spot as a precaution. When the results arrived days later, the doctor called, stating he needed to see my papaw in his office very soon. Upon arrival, the doctor presented my papaw with news that would change his life forever . . . the diagnosis was esophageal cancer.

We learned that the gastrointestinal specialist had already sent in a referral to a cardiothoracic surgeon at the University of Kentucky hospital. Although the surgeon was expected to contact us immediately, it was three weeks before the office even called to schedule an appointment. Meanwhile, my whole family could only wait and worry.

In the meantime, another aunt of mine who lived in Nashville, Tennessee, became aware of the situation and took matters in hand. She contacted a healthcare team at Vanderbilt University that included a very kind cardiothoracic surgeon named Dr. Putnam, who took on my papaw's case. Once Dr. Putnam reviewed the pathology reports, he made my papaw an immediate appointment.

As a four-year-old, I was not really sure what was happening or how to react, but I knew my papaw was sick and he needed help. So I decided to learn how to help him with whatever he needed, or at least whatever I could do at such a young age. So, as was typical in our relationship, I stuck with him like glue. I never wanted to leave his side. It was difficult for me to know he had to leave home to go see this doctor, not knowing what would come next. So I accompanied him and my grandma on the trip to Nashville and stayed at my aunt's house while awaiting the appointment.

At that initial appointment, the doctor clearly explained the recommended treatment option and scheduled a second appointment for the procedure. The procedure would include cutting and lifting the cancerous tissue out of the esophagus to clear the cancer out of his system.

The initial surgery occurred in May. However, not long into the operation the surgeon discovered that the whole esophageal wall was affected by the cancerous tissue, and he would require multiple operations. The surgeon continued with the initial operation, attempting to remove as much of the cancer as possible. Another operation using the same procedure was performed in June. Realizing this approach would be unsuccessful, the doctor decided to create a whole new treatment plan.

The decision was made to try to stretch up the stomach to construct a new esophagus, which would be a tremendous undertaking. In August he went in for this long and treacherous operation, hoping it would complete his battle. After many sleepless nights in the hospital, he was released to return home. However, rather than immediately returning to Kentucky, we remained at my aunt's house to allow my papaw more time to rest and heal. During that time, specifically two weeks later in September, he faced a serious surgical complication. After spontaneously throwing up large amounts of blood, he was rushed to the ER at Vanderbilt. It was discovered that the new esophagus had adhered to his aorta and caused an aortic rupture. Surgery was performed to repair the rupture and he then began a very long rehabilitation process including an esophagostomy with routine tests, checkups, and home health assistance. But he had made it! However, as time went on, the esophagus began failing and not performing correctly. The next approach was to take a piece of his colon and stretch it for use as an esophagus. This procedure was performed the following March with very high hopes of a final solution. He came out of the operation facing a long-time process of healing and rehab. He had two tubes going into his stomach—one for feeding and one for medicating—as he could not put anything at all in his mouth until May. This was because his diabetes required a longer healing time for the new esophagus. In June, his stomach tubes were removed, and the family hoped he would find some peace and comfort going forward.

As often happens, everything was getting better until it started to get worse. My papaw began getting very sick, repeatedly, due to an absorption issue that stemmed from the cancer. Though the numerous sicknesses that came in the following years were not specifically cancer, they were attributed as effects of the cancer. His struggle never ceased, and in October 2015 he was placed in hospice at home. Sadly, after a long, hard fight, my best friend, my papaw, lost his battle on October 31, 2015.

"You may have lost your battle with cancer, but you are still my hero."

—unknown

CANCER IN KENTUCKY

Sadly, the experiences I have shared with you are only a small fraction of the way cancer has had an impact on Appalachia or even on my family. Although statistics indicate that cancer diagnoses and mortality rates have recently declined [1], cancer rates are still extremely high.

While there are many contributing factors to cancer in Appalachia, two preventable primary contributors are healthcare access and lifestyle choices. As for healthcare access, receiving adequate healthcare in rural Appalachian areas is a difficult issue for many people. One contributor to this situation is the fact that many people in these areas are financially restricted, barely able to cover the basic needs of subsistence, with little or no funds to put toward healthcare. Even those covered by insurance are often unable to bear the cost of co-pays, medications, or other uncovered expenses. Another important issue with healthcare access is the lack of healthcare centers. In my hometown of Olive Hill, Kentucky, there are two clinics, but they provide only family care practitioners. The closest specialist clinic is St. Claire Medical Center in Morehead, Kentucky, located 29 miles away. While that seems nearby, those who are financially limited can find it difficult to buy gasoline for frequent trips . . . assuming they even have a car. As for lifestyle choices, many controllable actions contribute to the cancer rate. These include such things as the use of tanning beds, tobacco, alcohol, illicit drugs, as well as unhealthy diets.

In the fight against cancer, the lack of healthcare access and the predominance of unhealthy lifestyle choices have a direct impact on both the prevention and successful treatment of disease.

FIX THAT PROBLEM

While I believe that the problems discussed above could not necessarily be abolished, I do feel they could be greatly reduced. In order to make this happen it would take some real help from our government leaders as well as involvement of the people . . . each and every person in Appalachia and beyond. The only way to overcome these barriers and the lifestyles leading to cancer is to encourage permanent changes for everyone. I am a believer that these changes should include some degree of free health insurance for all people, or at least free/affordable standard medical visits and exams for those in need. Although this would help with healthcare access, we also need to address the issues occurring outside of medical facilities, and by this I am referring to the health behaviors of Appalachian people.

To reduce cancer rates, it is necessary to encourage healthy lifestyles . . . in other words, we need to address the previously mentioned issues of tanning beds, tobacco, alcohol, illicit drugs, as well as unhealthy diets. I believe the best approach would be instilling good lifestyle choices in youth, before the bad habits are acquired.

Tanning bed use, particularly beginning at an early age, is a serious problem. Appalachian youth are no different than youth from other regions in embracing the belief that they are invincible. As a result, their concern typically lies more with their current appearance than their chance of developing cancer later in life. In fact, many teens I know begin tanning around the age of 13 which, according to the Skin Foundation, makes them 69 percent more susceptible to developing basal cell carcinoma before the age of 40 [2]. In order to break this cycle, I believe tanning bed use should be regulated, requiring a legal ID proving that one is the age of 16 or older. We could also consider some sort of regulations for people of all ages.

The issue of tobacco and drug use spans generations, but many teens either use substances frequently or have at least experimented. As tobacco used to be a cash crop all over this region, as well as part of the culture, it was common for teens to start chewing and/ or smoking tobacco at a young age. However, in the current time, growing tobacco is not nearly as common as what it used to be.

Though there is an age limit for buying tobacco products, which was just recently raised, it still does not stop adults from buying them for underage users or stop cashiers from illegally selling to minors. I believe that there should be high consequences for adults or cashiers guilty of these actions. For the adult population, I believe there should be higher regulation on tobacco product use in some way. Also, broad advertising of the health risks might perhaps change many people's minds on using harmful tobacco products.

Another large problem in Appalachia is unhealthy dietary choices leading to obesity. Many of the people who make up Appalachia's population are in fact obese. While obesity may not seem like that big of a deal to the average person, it in fact leads to many other health issues, including cancer. A great reason for such high obesity rates in Appalachia is because healthy diets are usually not feasible to the general population. Healthy foods are expensive. Also, foods that are not homegrown are often filled with additives and preservatives which make these foods unhealthy and a potential leading factor to obesity [3]. It seems as if resolving this issue should be quite simple; however, it needs to be grasped soon! I believe, first and foremost, there should be legislation that would provide guidance to stop the use of market-sold additives and preservatives on homegrown foods. Eating a preservative widely used in breads, baked goods, and cheese may trigger metabolic responses that are linked to obesity and diabetes. I believe, as well, that another form of legislation should be passed in order to help low-income families afford healthy foods.

Though we can face many barriers when trying to protect ourselves from cancer, I have a great hope that the people of Appalachian Kentucky can figure out how to protect and care for one another. But in order to do this, we ALL must take action!

CONCLUSION

Through the Appalachian Career Training in Oncology (ACTION) Program, I am one of 20 high school students who have been chosen to take action on the cancer crisis in Appalachia! Though we are all different, we have one thing in common. That one thing is our dream to defeat this terrible cancer epidemic, take care of people in the area, and enhance the quality of life for the people who have already been taken over by this terrible disease. The stories you have just read are about how cancer has impacted me and my family. These stories are what inspired me to become the person I am today. Those cases are what inspired me to take action and apply for the ACTION Program. Because of my experiences, I have also decided that I would like to attend college in pursuit of a career in cardiothoracic surgery.

Remember to stay happy, stay healthy, stay safe, and take action whenever you get the chance. CANCER IS COMING SOMETIME IN YOUR LIFE, WHETHER YOU EXPECT IT OR NOT!

REFERENCES

1. "State Cancer Profiles," National Cancer Institute, 2020, https://statecancerprofiles.cancer.gov/recenttrend/index.php?0&4221&9599&001&999&00&1#results.

2. A. Venosa, "Teen Tanning: A Short-Term Decision with Long-Term Consequences," Skin Cancer Foundation, April 2, 2018, https://www.skincancer.org/blog/tanning/.

3. A. Norton, "Could Common Food Preservative Make People Fat?" WebMD, 2005, www.webmd.com/diet/news/20190424/could-common-food-preservative-make-people-fat#1.

THE KENTUCKY KILLER: CANCER

Hanah Whisenant

"To expect the unexpected shows a thoroughly modern intellect."
—Oscar Wilde

My name is Hanah Whisenant. I am from Louisa, Kentucky, where I attend Lawrence County High School. I plan to one day become a surgeon. I have aspired to work in the healthcare field since I was very young. Whenever my grandmother had a doctor's appointment, I would tag along simply to gain more medical knowledge. I can't remember a time when I was not captivated by science and medicine. For Christmas, I would ask for anatomical models instead of toys. I would study medical terminology and surgical techniques for fun. One specific topic that piqued my interest was cancer. It seemed like such a common occurrence in my community, which made me curious. Why were so many people in my life being diagnosed with cancer?

Unfortunately, I've known more than my fair share of people who have had cancer. Here are some of their stories. A close family friend, James, was diagnosed with lung cancer not too long ago. He underwent extremely harsh and life-sucking treatments for a very long time. It was difficult to watch him go through this because he feels like family. James has always been there for me, ever since I was very little, and he has done so much for me in my lifetime. Just when we thought he was in the clear, doctors told him that his lung cancer had come back. This was devastating news, and I couldn't bear the thought of watching him go through those treatments again. James began immunotherapy—a type of cancer treatment—to try and beat cancer once and for all. To this day, he is still fighting against lung cancer, and he is doing everything he can to overcome it.

Also, my Mamaw Rachel was diagnosed with cervical cancer years ago. Luckily, she overcame it—although there were various struggles along the way. She went through many rounds of chemo and radiation therapy. These treatments are known to be very brutal to a person. Because of her insurance coverage, she had to settle for a mediocre medication. With the odds set against my mamaw, she still beat cancer.

Furthermore, my Great-Aunt Tammy started smoking at a very early age. This inevitably led to lung cancer. Tammy struggled with lung cancer for less than a year. It was discovered very late, and she was diagnosed at stage four. She passed away soon after due to pneumonia.

Still, the diagnosis that affected me the most was my grandma's. Brenda Sue Whisenant was healthy for the majority of her life. Every time I saw her, she was ready to go for a walk outside and enjoy nature. When I heard that my grandma was in the hospital, I was in disbelief. My mind jumped to terrifying situations—that she had been in an accident, had taken a fall, or worse. My family was informed that my grandma just had a cold. Later, doctors found a vast amount of fluid in her lungs. This led them to believe she had pneumonia. My grandma was kept in the hospital for days while doctors continuously drained the fluid from her lungs. After an even longer period, the doctors discovered that my grandma had metastatic cancer. This fact was very distressing for my family to hear. After all, we arrived at the hospital thinking my grandma had a slight cold. She passed away shortly after. This just goes to show how truly unexpected cancer is. Nobody expects for this killer disease to wreck their lives. Nobody expects to have their loved ones taken away in such a harsh, brutal manner. After the passing of my grandmother, my interest in oncology became even more prominent. I became very curious about how cancer works, how it grows, how it spreads, and how it kills. In particular, I was curious about why cancer impacted Kentucky residents so harshly. Kentucky is the leading state in the number of cancer cases [1].

There are numerous factors that can cause cancer, including even the most unsuspected events. A major contributor to the cancer problem in Kentucky is that many Kentuckians are simply unaware. Many Kentuckians never consult a doctor, even if they are experiencing symptoms. A lot of Kentucky residents just never learn about cancer and the effects of the disease. It is quite easy to ignore this topic if you are completely blind to it. If a person does not know of the true causes of cancer, they will not find it necessary to be screened or treated. Another cause is the use of tobacco products. There are poisons and cancer-causing chemicals in tobacco products that damage cells and weaken the immune system, making it harder for the body to kill cancerous cells. When this happens, cancer cells grow and multiply uncontrollably. As it happens, Kentucky has one of the highest percentages of tobacco users in the United States. According to the Centers for Disease Control and Prevention, more than 20 percent of Kentuckians smoke cigarettes. In other states, like California and Utah, the smoking rate is much lower, with only about 10 percent of the population using these products [2]. These percentages say a lot about why cancer is so common in Kentucky.

Yet another cause of cancer is exposure to radon. As reported by the American Cancer Society, radon will break down into miniscule radioactive elements that linger in the lining of the lungs. These tiny radioactive particles emit radiation in the body. This radiation can eventually lead to lung cancer [3]. My home state of Kentucky ranks very high in levels of radon in the United States [4]. With a high level of radon comes a high number of cancer cases.

Even further, there is a direct link between obesity and cancer, so staying active could lower your chances of getting cancer. According to the National Cancer Institute, "Those who are overweight or obese are at greater risk for many diseases, including diabetes, high blood pressure, cardiovascular disease, stroke, and many cancers" [5].

Because all of these cancer-inducing events seem so common, it is easy to think cancer is inevitable. But there are numerous ways to prevent this disease. One of the best precautions to take in this situation is to "expect the unexpected." If we Kentuckians are aware of our situation, and if we take steps to prevent this awful disease from reaching us, we can undoubtedly save many lives. A clear way to potentially prevent cancer in Kentucky is lowering the number of smokers. This is obviously not an easy task for many people, but it is quite necessary. If you don't have to, try not to start smoking. It is extremely addictive, and once you start, it is very difficult to stop. If you've already picked up the habit, there are countless resources available to quit smoking. Just to name a few, there are nicotine patches, nicotine gum, and even pills.

Also, an effective way to possibly ward off cancer is getting active. Keeping active can help people stay at a healthy weight or lose weight. It can also lower the risk of heart disease, diabetes, stroke, high blood pressure, osteoporosis, and certain cancers, as well as reduce stress and boost mood. Inactive (sedentary) lifestyles do just the opposite [6]. We are constantly up and about, so it shouldn't be too hard to fit some exercise into your life. Some great ways of staying active are walking, dancing, and even cleaning.

Another way to prevent cancer is outreach to inform others of cancer risk factors. Whether it is pinning a pamphlet to a bulletin board or talking to people as they leave the grocery store, outreach is vital. Outreach improves cancer literacy, which can decrease the chance of actually getting cancer. It is really quite simple to spread the word in your community. A very effective way to get people's attention is food. Set up a table filled with healthy snacks at a popular location in your community. While people are reaching for a refreshment, offer them an informative flyer about cancer and how to prevent it. Another way to reach out to your community is hanging up flyers. Place a flyer or two around a very populated area. More people will look at the flyer if it is posted in a busy area. A good example is at the grocery store or a fast-food restaurant. Yet another way to spread awareness in your community is by using social media. It is nearly impossible to find a person—especially a teenager—who doesn't have social media. Something as simple as a post on Facebook can open someone's eyes to view cancer as what it really is—a disease that can be prevented. A major benefit to outreach on social media is the ease of sharing. With just a click of a button, your message can be reposted on someone else's profile. This allows even more people to see the information and share it with their friends. As this cycle continues, more and more people will learn about cancer and how to prevent it. Clearly, when more people are knowledgeable of the risk factors of cancer, more people will try to avoid them. More people will visit a doctor regularly if they are aware that cancer can be prevented. This is why outreach is crucial. As you can see, there are numerous ways to lower the number of cancer cases in Kentucky.

To summarize, cancer is a brutal disease that impacts my

home state of Kentucky the hardest. Because of a high number of smokers and tobacco users, refusing to visit a doctor, low cancer literacy and lack of general cancer knowledge, obesity, and many other factors, Kentucky seems predisposed to cancer. But there are many ways to overcome this horrible disease, such as lowering the number of smokers and helping people quit smoking, getting active and exercising more regularly, and reaching out to your community to provide knowledge and raise awareness. In conclusion, cancer affects Kentucky very harshly, but there are ways to potentially prevent it.

REFERENCES

1. R. L. Siegel et al., "Cancer Statistics, 2021," *CA: A Cancer Journal for Clinicians* 71, no. 1 (January–February 2021): 7–33, https://acsjournals.onlinelibrary.wiley.com/doi/10.3322/caac.21654.

2. "Map of Current Cigarette Use among Adults," Centers for Disease Control and Prevention, 2018, https://www.cdc.gov/statesystem/cigaretteuseadult.html.

3. "Radon and Cancer," American Cancer Society, 2015, https://www.cancer.org/cancer/cancer-causes/radiation-exposure/radon.html.

4. "Radon Levels by State, 2021," World Population Review, 2021, https://worldpopulationreview.com/state-rankings/radon-levels-by-state.

5. "Obesity and Cancer," National Cancer Institute, 2021, https://www.cancer.gov/about-cancer/causes-prevention/risk/obesity/obesity-fact-sheet.

6. "Obesity Prevention Source," Harvard School of Public Health, 2021, https://www.hsph.harvard.edu/obesity-prevention-source/obesity-causes/physical-activity-and-obesity/.

MEMORIES NEVER MADE

Zane Whitaker

Grandparents are an important part of families in Eastern Kentucky. They oftentimes are the glue that holds families together and ensures that traditions continue. Unfortunately, I was never able to know my maternal grandfather because he passed away from prostate cancer when I was only 11 months old. I also lost my paternal great-grandmother to colon cancer when I was around four years old. I have heard many wonderful stories and have seen pictures of Christmas gatherings but I am unable to recall any specific memories of her. Cancer steals from families. It robs them of wisdom, advice, memories, hugs, traditions, and more.

I can imagine what it would have been like following my grandfather around on his farm. I love animals, and he had plenty, from what I have been told. Horses, cattle, chickens, ducks, dogs, and cats, to name a few. He loved his animals and was very active his entire life on the farm. He also raised tobacco as a hobby. He enjoyed working in his tobacco crop. He was never a smoker and actually detested smoking. I have been told that I look like him. I am tall, with the same type of slender build. I have his thick, coarse hair, but it is not the same color. We also had other similarities.

He did not drink "pop," as we call it in Eastern Kentucky, or soft drinks, as others call it. I don't drink "pop" either. I love milk with all food, and so did he. Stories are nice, but I wish that I could have had these experiences with him and been able to see the similarities for myself. I don't even remember meeting him, because cancer stole those memories and the relationship that we could have had.

I have been told that my great-grandmother, who died from colon cancer, was the glue that held family traditions together. We still gather at Christmastime with my great-uncles and aunt and cousins to attempt to continue what my great-grandmother started. I don't remember her, but I can still feel the love that she had for her family and can look back at pictures of gatherings past. I know that she would have been proud of me, as she was of all her grandchildren.

Hi, I'm Zane Whitaker, I'm 15 and live in the small county of Magoffin. Magoffin County has a little less than 12,000 people, so I would consider it quite small. This year I will begin my sophomore year at Magoffin County High School. Last year wasn't the best for beginning my high school experience because we had to begin the year taking virtual classes because of COVID. Later, in the middle of the year, we began hybrid classes. Students were split into three groups, having the kids who wanted to return in person either go on Monday and Tuesday or Thursday and Friday. The three days that students wouldn't be in person would still be virtual, but students also had the option of staying completely virtual. Finally, after the pandemic became somewhat under control, we returned to school without any virtual classes. We were also able to compete in sports this year. Last school year was quite distinct to say the least, and not in a good way. Last year was so different, and many struggled to adapt to the new virtual learning. I didn't struggle to adapt, but I wasn't exactly gleeful about the new learning circumstances. Everyone made do with the virtual learning, but it didn't feel like learning; instead it felt like something to keep us busy. Now, with the COVID vaccine released, things will hopefully return to normal, or at least as normal as they can be.

Before the pandemic happened, I was introduced to a program by a guest speaker. That speaker was Chris Prichard, who is the program coordinator for the Appalachian Career Training in Oncology (ACTION) Program. I was immediately interested and started researching. I was excited, to say the least, and when I submitted my application, I was excited to see if I would be accepted. When I was told the good news, I was super excited, and I couldn't wait to see what the future held for me in the ACTION Program. This opportunity has given me a voice and a chance to share my story with others in Appalachia and beyond.

Similar to many who live in Eastern Kentucky, I have been forced to deal with the effects of cancer on a family member. I've dealt with it a multitude of times, and although I have not lost anyone to cancer in recent memory, cancer has robbed me of creating memories with loved ones. Cancer took two people from me, at the age of 11 months and then again at four years of age, that would have been important in my development and upbringing. As devastating as my losses have been, I have friends that have suffered substantial losses recently. I have at least two friends that are currently experiencing the effects of cancer in their immediate families, one of those being a close friend that lost his mother to breast cancer just this year and another whose mother has recently been diagnosed with breast cancer.

Although I have not lost anyone in recent memory, my aunt had a scare with skin cancer two years ago. She had a place that came up over her upper lip. She did not think that it was anything serious but eventually had it checked out by a dermatologist. They determined it was basal cell carcinoma. She had to have it removed, which left a scar, but she was lucky that a scar is all that she was left with. My aunt has always loved the sun and does not use sunscreen as recommended. This led to her developing basal cell carcinoma. Luckily, she did not need further treatment such as chemotherapy or radiation. Her husband had been diagnosed with melanoma before they were ever married, which was a result of his many years lifeguarding at the local pool. Both of these stories reverberate simple steps that can—such as applying sunscreen—be taken to help prevent some types of cancer.

Even though many types of cancer are preventable, Kentucky has some of the highest cancer incidence rates and death rates in the nation [1]. Kids, preteens, and teens all have very impressionable minds, and this is due to their brains still developing. The brain on average is done developing at age 25 [2]. While a youth's brain is still developing, I believe that this time should be taken advantage of by implementing a standard in school on how cancer forms and functions and why it is so dangerous. It is important to teach kids about cancer early, and especially tobacco use and its correlation to cancer, because once you start using tobacco, it is very difficult to stop. Nicotine, a highly addictive chemical found in tobacco, combined with other harmful chemicals in cigarettes and tobacco products is what makes tobacco use so dangerous [3]. Education and awareness could just be the difference between teens choosing to smoke, chew, or vape, and could save them from going down a regrettable path.

There are so many ways that you can protect yourself, yet so many people choose to ignore precautions and recommendations. They often think "This could not happen to me" or "I'll be fine this time." It may be that they are not educated or aware of simple preventive measures they can take or what regular health screenings they should receive. Whether it be ignoring recommendations such as wearing sunscreen, like my aunt and uncle, deciding to smoke even when you know the consequences, or not receiving regular checkups, these actions can lead to unwanted and harmful health effects.

Screenings are an important part of prevention. They are used to detect cancer and to hopefully catch it at an early stage so that minimal treatment is required. Screenings for prostate cancer are recommended starting at age 50 for men of average risk [4]. Colon cancer screenings for people of average risk are recommended starting at age 45 [5]. Skin cancer screenings are not based on age. The Skin Cancer Foundation recommends annual checkups with a dermatologist unless you have risk factors that place you at higher risk [6]. I chose to highlight the preventive screenings of these three types of cancers because they occurred within my family and I will need to be aware of my risk and when to start screening.

Poverty is related to obtaining adequate healthcare such as preventive screenings for cancer. We know that poverty affects many Kentucky families. It can affect the families' personal well-being by leaving them unable to afford healthcare or simple necessities like groceries. Less money means less nutritious foods, less knowledge about illness and medicine, fewer doctors' visits and dental visits, less preventive healthcare, and less quality medical attention [7]. Poverty affects 16.3 percent of the total Kentucky population, which is a total of 703,627 people, which ranks the state 48th in the nation in poverty [8]. Poverty is even more prevalent in Eastern Kentucky, with Magoffin County having the highest unemployment rate in the state at 11.7 percent [9].

Poverty, unequal access to education, employment, and barriers to healthcare and other resources are disparities that have a prominent presence in Eastern Kentucky [10]. Adult health is strongly linked to economic well-being, and central Appalachians (Eastern Kentucky in particular) are in poor health relative to other Americans including other rural Americans [11]. This is important, especially in the battle with cancer. Death rates due to cancer are falling over time in the United States, but they are not falling as fast in Appalachia, and the rate in central Appalachia has been relatively constant [12, 13]. This is due to the fact that people in poverty are more likely to be uninformed, or even if they are educated on cancer, it is likely they are unable to afford the proper screenings they need to help catch cancer at an early stage, or worse, they may be unable to afford the proper treatment.

This disease affects so many people, and that number continues to climb in Appalachia. While some cancers are unpreventable, whether it be contracting cancer through genetics or just an unlucky stream of events, some are preventable. For example, most lung and bronchus cancers are contracted through tobacco use [14]. Tobacco products are easily accessible, even though they can have life-threatening consequences. Today, people are still using these products even if they know the consequences. The American Cancer Society estimates that there will be around 4,970 lung and bronchus cancer cases in Kentucky in 2021. That's almost one-sixth of the estimated cancer cases in the state of Kentucky [1]!

I believe it is important to highlight just how important it is to take action to reduce cancer rates in Appalachia. The rates here are among the highest in the nation and need to be addressed. As stated before, you should take proper preventive steps to reduce your likelihood of developing cancer and receive screenings when you are of the right age (or your doctor recommends to do so). It is also important to receive regular checkups with your doctor. Also, the role of poverty and other health disparities that exist at higher rates in Appalachia cannot be ignored.

I am fortunate to not have witnessed the life-threatening effects of cancer. Other than immediate family that unfortunately I could not meet and my aunt and uncle's run-ins with skin cancer, I have not had many experiences with cancer, and for that I am very thankful. I hope this essay will lead others to strive for change and be proactive within their communities while also taking preventive steps themselves. I am hopeful that one day I will be able to live in a world where Appalachia is not among the highest in the nation in cancer rates, that someday cancer will be stopped and no longer able to steal more memories than it already has.

REFERENCES

1. "Cancer Statistics Center: Kentucky at a Glance," American Cancer Society, accessed 2021, https://cancerstatisticscenter.cancer.org/#!/state/Kentucky.

2. "Brain Maturity Extends Well beyond Teen Years," National Public Radio, 2011, cited January 27, 2021, https://www.npr.org/templates/story/story.php?storyId=141164708#:~:text=Brain%20Maturity%20Extends%20Well%20Beyond%20Teen%20Years%20Under%20most%20laws,maturity%20until%20the%20age%2025.

3. "Is Nicotine Addictive?" National Institute on Drug Abuse, 2020, https://www.drugabuse.gov/publications/research-reports/tobacco-nicotine-e-cigarettes/nicotine-addictive.

4. "American Cancer Society Recommendations for Prostate Cancer Early Detection," American Cancer Society, 2020, https://www.cancer.org/cancer/prostate-cancer/detection-diagnosis-staging/acs-recommendations.html.

5. "American Cancer Society Guideline for Colorectal Cancer Screening," American Cancer Society, 2020, https://www.cancer.org/cancer/colon-rectal-cancer/detection-diagnosis-staging/acs-recommendations.html.

6. "Annual Exams," Skin Cancer Foundation, 2020, https://www.skin-cancer.org/early-detection/annual-exams/.

7. J. Rieman and P. Leighton, *The Rich Get Richer and the Poor Get Prison:*

Ideology, Class, and Criminal Justice, 9th ed. (Boston: Allyn & Bacon, 2010).

8. "Kentucky Report—2020," Talk Poverty, 2021, https://talkpoverty. org/state-year-report/kentucky-2020-report/.

9. "State Releases County Unemployment Data for June 2020," Kentucky.gov, 2020, https://kentucky.gov/Pages/Activity-stream.aspx-?n=EducationCabinet&prId=429#:~:text=Magoffin%20County%20 recorded%20the%20state's,Perry%20counties%2C%206.9%20 percent%20each.

10. A. Rogers, *Human Behavior in the Social Environment*, 5th ed. (New York: Routledge, 2019).

11. J. Ziliak, *Appalachian Legacy: Economic Opportunities After the War on Poverty* (Washington, DC: Brookings Institute Press, 2012).

12. L. Gilpin, "Cancer Rates Are Dropping—But Not in Rural Appalachia," FiveThirtyEight, February 14, 2017, https://fivethirtyeight. com/features/cancer-rates-are-dropping-but-not-in-rural-appalachia/.

13. N. Yao, "Cancer Disparities in Rural Appalachia: Incidence, Early Detection, and Survivorship," *Journal of Rural Health* 33, no. 4 (2017): 375–381.

14. "What are the Risk Factors for Lung Cancer?" Centers for Disease Control and Prevention, 2020, www.cdc.gov/cancer/lung/basic_info/ risk_factors.htm.

RISK AND CONSEQUENCES

Carolene Willhoite

You never realize how big of a risk something is until you have met the outcome. This is what it is like for those who are diagnosed with cancer; whether it be lung, breast, ovarian, or other variations of the disease, as the devastating list goes on and on. Cancer affects so many people: roughly 1.8 million people in the United States were estimated to be diagnosed to have cancer in 2020 [1]. Nearly 2 million people does not seem like a lot compared to the 330 million people that live in the United States, but 1.8 million people is just a few thousand more than live in Phoenix, Arizona. I want you to imagine the equivalent of an entire major metropolitan city gone because of cancer. And then we also must look at where cancer rates are the highest: Kentucky.

Kentucky's cancer rate, which stands at 519.6 people diagnosed per every group of 100,000, is horrifying. In 2021 alone, Kentucky is estimated to have 30,270 new cases and 10,090 fatalities [2, 3]. This data is alarming, as it means thousands of people are expected to be diagnosed with cancer and thousands will also die. Things such as certain health behaviors lead to many cancer cases as well as deaths. However, the physical and political environment also does not help matters. Within this essay, I will speak on my personal experience with cancer, Kentucky's cancer statistics, the health behaviors and the risk factors contributing to the high rates of cancer, and how the disease could be prevented.

MY PERSONAL EXPERIENCE

My name is Carolene Willhoite, a name given to me by my parents to honor my late grandmother, Carolene Pelfrey ("Mama"). In 1994, Mama passed away from breast cancer. Being born on October 12th of 2005, 11 years after her death, I never got to meet her. I never got the chance to go shopping with her or bake cookies, sew, practice music with her, or wear goofy outfits she would have gotten me. I never got to experience any of that with her, because breast cancer stripped her from this world. We think that this cancer formed from something so simple: estrogen. My grandmother was prescribed estrogen pills when she began menopause to help balance her hormone levels. Little did she know these pills would kill her.

Mama was taken away from her siblings, her husband, and her children, including her youngest child and only daughter, Jean-Ann, who is my mother, and later in life, her grandchildren, nephews, and nieces. Mama, I have been told, was an amazing woman. She was joyful, stunning, a great cook, and a kind friend. She was a good person, one who didn't deserve to have been taken so soon.

Although I never met my grandmother, you may wonder why her death due to cancer affects me so much, and it is because I feel connected to her. Not because we share the same name, but because I have followed in her same path. I feel as though she is with me, not physically, but I feel she is there. I will always love and cherish her. Her story is why I write this: to reach out to others who do not deserve to lose a loved one to cancer.

THE GAP

As I have stated earlier, Kentucky is estimated to have 30,270 new cancer cases this year [2, 3]. You may be wondering, where are most of the cancer cases coming from in Kentucky? The answer is Appalachian Kentucky. Appalachia is on the eastern side of the state, and it is a very rural area. Due to it being rurally located, the area lacks proper education opportunities and has low access to medical care. The population is also not necessarily the wealthiest. Some people in the area are employed as farmers or work in other areas of agriculture and may not make that much money. This said, the high cancer rates mainly reflect how the population acts. Being second-highest in tobacco production in the United States, Kentucky has a major impact on the tobacco industry, and tobacco has a cultural influence on its citizens as a result. Due to this influence of the tobacco industry, many citizens end up using tobacco products, which leads to the possibility of many becoming addicted to tobacco.

Tobacco addiction often leads to lung cancer, which is often fatal here in Kentucky. One reason for this is because cancer centers and hospitals are not that accessible for Appalachian Kentucky residents. This is a dangerous factor, as many who may require urgent care have a harder time trying to access it. The result of not having a nearby hospital/cancer facility can cost a person their life. In addition, many people may not have insurance in rural areas like Appalachian Kentucky, and treating cancer or simply just going to get a screening costs an abundance of money. The cost already keeps people from going to get a preventive screening; therefore, people are even less likely to battle cancer once being diagnosed, due to the extreme cost. As I have already stated, some people in this area rely on agricultural work. Insurance may not be offered to some workers, or what insurance a person has may not cover the cost of cancer prevention or cancer treatments.

Schools in Kentucky are also not properly educating students about the consequences of smoking and drinking. As a student who has gone through the education system in both Morgan County, Kentucky and Montgomery County, Kentucky, I can vouch that thorough education on topics such as drinking and smoking has not been covered. Sadly, most of the education on these topics consists of short and vague lessons. The first lesson I was given was in first grade, and it was short and only taught one simple aspect of smoking. "It leads to cancer" was how the educator taught it, but that was not enough for a true understanding of what smoking is and what it does to your body. A similar lesson was given for alcohol. After my first-grade year, I was never taught or introduced to a cancer prevention topic again until my freshman year of high school in health class. However, like the lesson I had received many years before, it was short and vague and just dived straight into the simple fact that smoking leads to cancer; it left out important information such as treatments and other health effects. So the curriculum and education are lacking; they do not provide enough information to have a child understand what smoking and drinking truly does to your body. Yes, smoking *can* lead to cancer, but is that enough to educate, or say scare, a child away from using tobacco products or drinking? It is not, or else smoking rates in this state would most certainly decrease. The curriculum in cancer education needs to be reformed.

I must mention that although lung cancer is the highest contributor to cancer deaths in Kentucky, it is not the only cancer that causes many deaths in the state. The *Courier-Journal* says, "Kentucky's death rates also rank in the Top 10 nationally for breast, colorectal and cervical cancers" [4, 5]. Ultimately, our situation is simply a crisis; many lives are being taken due to the lack of healthcare access, the cost to prevent and treat the disease, and the lack of cancer education. Kentucky residents just are not getting the same chances and education to both treat and avoid cancer.

RISKS AND PROTECTION

What do you do daily? Possibly eat a pan-fried meal or smoke a few cigarettes? Do you maybe go to the tanning bed once a week for 30 minutes or so? And after all this, you possibly sit down and have a glass of wine or another alcoholic beverage, by chance?

Everything I just listed are called "health behaviors," which are activities you do that affect your physical and mental health. These health behaviors are some that can cause cancer and are major contributors in doing so. These behaviors can eat at you, consume you by messing up, or otherwise known as "mutating," your DNA.

The pan-fried meal could lead to colorectal cancer, smoking can result in lung cancer, wine or other alcohol can lead to liver cancer, and the tanning bed can lead to skin cancer. Yes, our everyday habits that are so simple can lead to something so deadly as cancer. And what about other risk factors?

Your age, gender, weight, and genetics are all risk factors that can make it more possible for you to get cancer. As you age, your immune system and body get weaker and more prone to cancer. If you are female, you have a chance of developing such cancers as breast, cervical, or ovarian cancer. You can also simply just be born with the chance to develop cancer later in life due to mutations in your genes that your parents passed down to you. Little things such as those that just make you who you are can affect your risk of getting cancer. What seems so normal may not be so.

Weight within Kentucky is also a large contributor to cancer. Kentucky is ranked sixth in the nation for obesity [6]. This can be due to cultural patterns such as eating fast food, lack of exercise, and not having the financial support to eat healthier options. The lack of proper education and resources is also a major reason for these high rates. Obesity does not help our cancer situation, as it makes it far harder to battle it. According to the CDC, obesity can cause cancer by causing higher hormone levels and higher insulin levels as well as causing inflammation. The more overweight you are and the longer you stay overweight, the higher your chances of developing cancer are [7]. Already-existing obesity levels in a patient can lead to further complications in cancer patients.

And with that, you may be wondering: how do we prevent cancer? You keep your health behaviors and risk factors in check. You get cancer screenings, you diet and exercise, and you take better care of your body. You start wearing more sunscreen and avoid tanning beds, you throw away that pack of Marlboros, and you consume healthier foods. You do what you can to protect your body. Of course, age, gender, and genetics cannot be helped, but simply taking care of your body will improve your odds of avoiding cancer or beating it if you get it.

CONCLUSION

In this essay, I spoke to you of my grandmother, Mama, who died of breast cancer and whom I will never meet. I also spoke of cancer in Kentucky and how the situation and environment of our state do not help our situation. And lastly, I spoke to you about your health behaviors, other risk factors, and how to take better care of yourself. Please take care of yourself. Cancer may seem like something small from an outsider's point of view, but how do you think a loved one will feel if they learn you will not beat cancer? We all must be careful and avoid cancer risks to better balance the consequences toward lowering cancer rates in Kentucky.

REFERENCES

1. "Cancer Statistics at a Glance," Centers for Disease Control and Prevention, 2021, https://www.cdc.gov/nchs/pressroom/sosmap/cancer_mortality/cancer.htm.

2. "Facts & Figures 2021 Reports Another Record-Breaking 1-Year Drop in Cancer Deaths," American Cancer Society, 2021, https://www.cancer.org/latest-news/facts-and-figures-2021.html.

3. "Cancer Statistics Center: Kentucky at a Glance," American Cancer Society, accessed 2021, https://cancerstatisticscenter.cancer.org/#!/state/Kentucky.

4. "Cancer Kills Kentuckians at Highest Rate (Update)," North American Association of Central Cancer Registries, updated March 28, 2016, https://www.naaccr.org/cancer-kills-kentuckians-at-highest-rate/.

5. L. Ungar, "Cancer Kills Kentuckians at Highest Rate," *Louisville Courier-Journal*, December 17, 2015, https://www.courier-journal.com/story/life/wellness/health/2015/12/17/cancer-kills-kentuckians-highest-rate-nation/74874698/.

6. "America's Health Rankings Annual Report," United Health Foundation, 2019, https://www.americashealthrankings.org/.

7. "Obesity and Cancer," National Cancer Institute, 2021, https://www.cancer.gov/about-cancer/causes-prevention/risk/obesity/obesity-fact-sheet.

UNDERGRADUATE STUDENT ESSAYS

AN OUTSIDER'S HOME

Haseeb Ahmad

Unlike most, my story doesn't start in Kentucky. I was originally born in the metropolis of Houston, Texas. I remember when my father first told me that we would be moving to Pikeville, Kentucky. I was completely shocked and quite stubborn because I did not want to move to a town that no one had ever heard of. Finally, after constant fighting and pleading with my family, I recognized that I was not going to win this battle.

After our move to Kentucky, I remember experiencing a complete culture shock. I was surrounded by hardworking, caring, and conservative people. The first thing I noticed was how fresh the air smelled and how nice the people were, but I also noticed how obese the majority of Kentuckians are. When my father told me that he had seen a record number of people in his heart clinic, I was not surprised. Many people seemed as if they were suffering from obesity, which led to an abundance of secondary problems. Regardless of my original feelings toward the move, I learned during my elementary and high school years that I would come to love the place that I now call home.

Being a minority in a prominently white neighborhood, I was mortified about making friends and finding a place to fit in. Yet the people accepted me as one of their own with their unmatched generosity and hospitality. As I grew up, this same community taught me the importance of family, faith, compassion, and hard work. When I was a senior in high school, I realized how much the community had given me and supported me in my dream of becoming a physician. I decided then and there that it was not fair for me to turn my back on these individuals who had given me so much, and I knew that if I was going to repay them, it would have to be through my role as a physician. Upon researching the public health of Kentucky, specifically Eastern Kentucky, I became extremely invested in the cancer epidemic of Kentucky.

One of the most interesting articles I stumbled upon was published by the *New York Times*, titled "What's the Matter with Eastern Kentucky?" [1] The negative tone and harsh words they used to describe the place I called home angered me greatly. Many of my peers viewed the article as an everyday occurrence and made remarks such as "What else is new?" This was not something I could take lightly, especially because of how it targeted my home. Here was an outsider, writing from an office hundreds of miles away in New York City, peering into my fellow Kentuckians' lives and pretending she understood. I remember talking to my English teacher and composing a letter to the author about the pain and misrepresentation shown in her article. Nonetheless, she ignored my letter and I never received a response. Although the article doesn't focus on cancer statistics in the area, it did focus on the value and permanence of life in Appalachia. The article described that six out of ten of the worst counties in the nation with respect to income, education, and obesity were in Eastern Kentucky [1]. In addition, a study published in 2017 found that in 2014, six of the highest cancer rates were in Eastern Kentucky counties [2]. Although the diction she used outraged me, it did shed light on the potential reasons that Eastern Kentucky is struggling with cancer rates.

Since I am not from the region, I was not aware of any family members or relatives that were affected by cancer. However, as I became more familiar with my school and community, I found that many of my new friends and classmates were not as fortunate. Almost all of them had immediate family members or close friends whose lives had been flipped upside down by cancer. A friend of mine was around 16 years old when the doctor told him that his mother had breast cancer. He was heartbroken, confused, and suffering, thinking that he might lose his mother to something he could not even see. Keeping in mind how important family and community is to Eastern Kentucky, this news hurt everyone in the city. Our community rallied to raise money, cook them food, and provide support to the whole family so they knew they were never alone.

This story is not unique, though. There were multiple cases where students found out their family members and friends had been diagnosed with cancer. In each case friends and peers always rushed to comfort them. It was a devastating occurrence each time, but the problem for me lay in how often I had experienced this. I began to wonder about my family history and found that obesity, heart disease, and even cancer ran in my family, but I was never aware because of the distance between me and my relatives. I learned that my great-grandfather had passed away from lung cancer and my great-grandmother had passed from complications of stomach cancer. All of this news was a shock to me and made me interested in researching how much my genetics would play a role in a potential cancer diagnosis in my future. This later led me to ask this question: what are the risk factors of cancer, and could they be the reason behind Eastern Kentucky's high cancer rates?

This is when I began looking into cancer and the statistics surrounding my home. The data may have been shocking to an outsider, but as someone who has been consistently surrounded by it, I was already expecting high numbers. When I looked at the national averages, I found that Kentucky's cancer incidence rates were high for many cancer types. When looking at the highest rates, I found that lung, colorectal, breast, and cervical cancers were at the top, with lung cancer leading the way [3]. Then I switched my focus to other diseases that are highly correlated with cancer, such as heart disease and obesity. According to America's health rankings, Kentucky was ranked 48th in heart disease, 50th in physical inactivity, and 46th in obesity [4]. What sticks out to me as a pre-medicine student is the fact that Kentucky is ranked last in physical inactivity. In the past two years that I have been attending the University of Kentucky, I have learned that exercise is the best medicine for preventing and decreasing so many different diseases. For example, cancer, cardiovascular disease, stroke, heart disease, and many other diseases are all related to obesity. If we could focus on helping people live more active lives, then we would likely see a decrease in cancer, not only in the Appalachian region but in all of Kentucky. In my opinion, I think exercise is one of the simplest and most effective ways to help Kentuckians. Just look at places like Colorado and New York, which are leading the way in physical activity. Is this the reason why places like Colorado and New York do not suffer at the same level of consequences? Although this answer is not simple, I do have a few ideas that I believe might help to explain the gap.

Kentucky is known as the Bluegrass State, and when you first ask people what they know about Kentucky, they will mention either our amazing basketball team or the Kentucky Derby. Yet what most people do not know is the beauty of the acres of hills, mountains, and farmland that can be found all over

Eastern Kentucky. However, Kentucky's beauty is sadly related to its ongoing health crisis. Major tobacco companies target this area because they know that these sprawling farms hold a rich history of growing tobacco. No matter if it is chewing tobacco, smoking, or some other form of nicotine product, I can guarantee you can find it anywhere in Eastern Kentucky. When driving in the car, the amount of advertising signs for tobacco is completely overwhelming. It is even more common in poverty-stricken communities, where the cycle starts with the parents exposing their kids to smoking and chewing tobacco. These kids are almost always taught that smoking and chewing is a part of their "culture." I remember in middle school when some kids would smoke and bring chewing tobacco to school to distribute to their friends. Sadly, at one point it seemed that if you wanted to be cool or "popular," you had to use some type of tobacco. My peers did not see the problem in this either; their teachers, more often than not, had the same addiction problem. If kids are watching their teachers, educators, friends, and role models trying these things, then how can we expect them to go down a better path? Kentucky's rich tobacco history and easy access to tobacco make the area an easy target for cancer.

Other problems, such as low economic diversity, high unemployment rates, high disability rates, and staggering poverty, tie into the cancer epidemic here. Considering all of these variables, it is no surprise that the Appalachian region also suffers from a lower life expectancy compared to the rest of the nation. All of these components have made the Appalachian region a hotspot for cancer to thrive and wreak havoc. However, I am very optimistic that we can still make the changes needed to help bring Eastern Kentucky out of this treacherous cycle.

Kentucky has some work to do, but if anyone can change these statistics, it's going to be the hardworking people of Eastern

Kentucky. So, what can we do to help Kentucky? I think two of the biggest areas that Eastern Kentucky can improve on is screening and education. Eastern Kentuckians do not go to the hospital until they absolutely need to, and this mindset is causing a lot of harm. One of the best ways to prevent cancer is to have yearly checkups and catch it early. If we could educate youth, they could encourage their family members to visit the doctor regularly. With this, who knows how many cancer deaths we could prevent. We also need to heavily focus on prevention. This starts with building a comprehensive program including exercise, eating healthy, avoiding tobacco, and discussing the benefits of a healthy lifestyle. If this training begins in early kindergarten and is continued through high school, it would allow enough time for kids to understand the importance of these things and make healthy habits early on. In addition to prevention, one thing that often gets overlooked is the lack of research completed by the healthcare workers of Eastern Kentucky. I think it would be well worth it to train doctors in Eastern Kentucky on how to find new and alternative ways to heal instead of simply prescribing another pill.

As my hometown continues to suffer at the hands of cancer, I find that it is not a choice for me to sit back and accept our suffering. There are innocent lives taken away from my fellow Kentuckians every year, many of which can be saved. As I continue my career in medicine and beyond, I will always try to be an advocate for my home. I am optimistic that I will instill real, long-term change in the near future.

REFERENCES

1. A. Lowrey, "What's the Matter with Eastern Kentucky?" *New York Times*, June 26, 2014, https://www.nytimes.com/2014/06/29/magazine/whats-the-matter-with-eastern-kentucky.html.

2. A. H. Mokdad, L. Dwyer-Lindgren, C. Fitzmaurice et al., "Trends and Patterns of Disparities in Cancer Mortality among US Counties, 1980–2014," *Journal of the American Medical Association* 317, no. 4 (2017): 388–406.

3. R. L. Siegel et al., "Cancer Statistics, 2021," *CA: A Cancer Journal for Clinicians* 71, no. 1 (January–February 2021): 7–33, https://acsjournals.onlinelibrary.wiley.com/doi/10.3322/caac.21654.

4. "America's Health Rankings Annual Report," United Health Foundation, 2019, https://www.americashealthrankings.org/.

UNDERSTANDING THE TOBACCO ADDICTION

Lindsay Bryant

Wake up, smoke a cigarette, start your day. This is the morning routine for many people in Eastern Kentucky, including my family. I grew up and went to school in Pineville, Kentucky. Pineville is located in southeastern Kentucky and is about a 20-minute drive away from the Kentucky-Tennessee border. I am now a junior at the University of Kentucky, majoring in public health and psychology on a pre-medicine track. I hope my experience challenges perceptions about tobacco addiction.

Growing up, I was always told how terrible smoking was and how I should never try even one puff of a cigarette. I understood, yet I was always confused as to why some of the most important people, like my mom and my dad, in my life didn't take their own advice. Why would they smoke when they told me how bad it was for my health? I couldn't understand why it was okay for them to do something that would cause them harm. After a few years of watching them do exactly what they told me not to, I began to get angry towards those around me who smoked cigarettes. As I got older, I learned how secondhand smoke could be harmful.

According to the CDC,

"Secondhand smoke causes nearly 34,000 premature deaths from heart disease each year in the United States among nonsmokers." [1]

This was another instance where I became angry about the people in my life smoking. Not only were they putting their own health at risk, but they were also putting my health at risk. I would get mad and beg my parents and grandparents to quit smoking. When they refused, I only got angrier. Why would they do something that could cause me harm? I remember telling my parents that if they loved me they would stop smoking. Looking back now, I said cruel things because I couldn't understand why cigarettes were so hard to give up. As a college student, I finally understand why many people continue to smoke despite having the knowledge that it is bad for their health.

I was always told that smoking is addictive, but I had a small understanding of what addiction really was. I always believed that a person could only be addicted to illegal things like drugs. In a sense, addiction to me meant something illegal. It baffled me that something legal could be so addicting. One clinical definition of addiction is:

"[Addiction is] a chronic, relapsing disorder characterized by compulsive drug seeking, continued use despite harmful consequences, and long-lasting changes in the brain." [2]

Nicotine is the drug in cigarettes. Nicotine can change the concentration of two chemicals in the brain, dopamine and norepinephrine [3, 4]. This change in concentration can cause a change in mood, which can be a positive mood change to smokers. This mood change may involve happiness, reduced stress, pleasure, and reduced anxiety. These alterations fit into the clinical definition of addiction. We also know that smoking has numerous harmful consequences such as increased risk of brain aneurysm, increased risk of heart attack, increased risk of stomach cancer, and much more [5]. This also fits into the clinical definition of addiction. This was one of the first factors that helped me to understand that even legal substances can be addictive.

The mood-altering substance, nicotine, is not the only factor that makes cigarettes so addictive. For many, smoking is a part of their way of life. From my personal experiences, many people in Eastern Kentucky started smoking when they were very young. Many began before they were even teenagers. To understand this, I started to think about the things that I have been doing since before I was a teenager. The first thing that came to my mind was eating chocolate, something I enjoy and that makes me happy despite knowing that too much of it can be bad for my health. Chocolate can affect your nervous and cardiovascular system when eaten in excess [6]. If I wanted to, I could stop eating chocolate, but it is something that I like to do and that I have been doing for a very long time. Thinking of this helped me to grasp the idea as to why some of my family did not want to quit smoking. They had been smoking since before they were teenagers, and it was something that they enjoyed. Though this does not excuse the choice to keep smoking, comparing it to my own experience helped me to understand that quitting is not easy.

I believe another reason people smoke, especially older individuals, is the influence of advertisements decades ago. Seventy years ago, cigarette ads had little to no restrictions. Many ads read like testimonials from doctors promoting the health benefits of smoking, or featured beautiful people with a lifestyle worth imitating, or used seemingly harmless cartoon characters to target children.

An ad for the Camel brand of cigarettes features a doctor smoking a cigarette with the caption "More doctors smoke Camels than any other cigarette" [7]. Another advertisement, for the brand Viceroys, featured a dentist with the caption "As your dentist, I would recommend Viceroys." There was even an advertisement that claimed, "Chesterfield cigarettes are just as pure as the water you drink." When the advertisements were not targeting adults with a doctor's approval, they were targeting young adults and children with ads that featured animal mascots like Joe Camel or ads that depicted young adults having fun while smoking. A specific ad for the brand Newport featured three young adults having fun by the water with the caption "Alive with pleasure." Cigarette companies also used beauty to market to individuals; they would feature a beautiful woman or a handsome man smoking cigarettes. Without restrictions on their advertisements, cigarette companies could market their product any way they wanted, even if it was not true. In 1970, President Nixon signed the Public Health Cigarette Smoking Act into law, banning cigarette ads from radio and television [8]. But by then, the damage had already been done. The number of people smoking peaked in the mid-1960s and did not start decreasing until the late 1970s [9]. Many of our parents and grandparents grew up watching these advertisements. They grew up thinking that cigarettes were approved by doctors and dentists. Cigarette companies targeted youth to ensure that they could create lifelong smokers. I learned about all of these different tactics in my public health courses. I came to realize that when my family members formed these habits, they didn't know that smoking was bad for their health. With the information we have today it is easy to criticize smokers, but when you think about what they grew up hearing and seeing from trusted sources, it is easier to understand why they began and eventually became addicted to smoking.

The reasons I listed above are not to be taken as excuses for people who smoke, but as reasons to understand why there is still such a high prevalence of smoking, especially in Kentucky. According to the CDC Behavioral Risk Factor Surveillance System (BRFSS) study in 2018, 23.4 percent of adults in Kentucky were current smokers [10]. In 2017, a survey showed that 14.3 percent of high school students in Kentucky used cigarettes [11]. Today we know that tobacco products are directly related to numerous diseases, including the top three leading causes of death in Kentucky: heart disease, cancer, and chronic lower respiratory diseases [5, 12, 13]. In 2018, Kentucky led the United States in deaths due to cancer, with a rate of 181.6 per 100,000 people; overall deaths were 10,135 [14]. Specifically, Kentucky's lung cancer incidence rate was 92.4 per 100,000 people, compared to the national incidence rate of 68.8 per 100,000 people [15]. Many people use these dire statistics to support claims that Kentuckians are unhealthy "hicks." While the statistics validate those claims, it fails to help others understand why Kentucky has those health statistics.

Born and raised in Eastern Kentucky, I have experienced these stereotypes firsthand when traveling. I have heard countless jokes about how Kentuckians are unhealthy because they are stupid. Many people assume that I smoke or ask if I "vape." I have heard that when it comes to health, Kentucky is hopeless and that people bring their bad health upon themselves with their bad habits. I disagree with this. "Hopeless" is a term that an outsider would use because they have not experienced the resilience of the people in Kentucky. Perpetuating a stereotype simply for laughs is a sign of not understanding who Kentuckians are. Understanding the culture and way of life is imperative to understanding the health of Kentuckians, including the alarming cancer rates. I believe that instead of criticism and stereotypes, we should support educational programs and our future doctors and educators. We should invest in our poor counties and ensure that children do not develop the same bad habits that their families may have. I believe that one of the most important educational experiences the youth in Kentucky could benefit from is seeing the damage that cigarettes can cause to their body. All too often teens dismiss the negative health effects of smoking because they cannot see what is actually happening to their bodies. These visuals of consequences would make the damage seem personal and authentic. Though many other factors contribute to the disease rates in Kentucky, we can start with the youth to make sure that smoking is no longer one of those factors.

There have been many initiatives to lower the smoking rates in Kentucky. There are laws such as one that prevents youth under 21 from buying tobacco products and any other alternatives, like e-cigarettes. There are punishments for youth that break this law as well as punishments for merchants that break the law. Though there isn't a statewide indoor smoking ban, many places in Kentucky have banned smoking in many indoor places. Most places have a designated smoking area for those that wish to smoke. Unless these smoking areas are outside, the smoke still infects the area. Having smoking areas only outdoors helps to ensure that everyone has access to clean air and that those who wish to smoke still have a place to do so. There is still much that we can do.

As a public health major, I think that prevention and education are the best approaches we can take to lower the rates of smoking. This prevention starts at home. Who do we admire most when we are children? My answer, like many others, would be my family. Many children and teenagers see their parents and their grandparents smoking and this leads them to believe that it is acceptable or cool for them to smoke. I believe that understanding why our parents and grandparents smoke is essential to prevent our youth from beginning to smoke. They may hear from outsiders that smoking is bad for them, but the influence of their family outweighs the advice they get from a stranger. I believe to counteract this way of life, education needs to be more than just "Smoking is bad for you and here are the diseases it can cause." Children and teenagers should get to learn the things that I learned in my college public health classes. We need to address that the information and laws we have today are not the same as our parents and grandparents had when they were young. This information can change how youth view the habits of their family. It can help them to understand that their parents did not know that smoking was bad for them when they started, and now they are addicted. Our youth need to understand that smoking isn't a "way of life" but something that our families started because it was advertised as a "stress reliever" and promoted by doctors. Education is essential in preventing a new generation from becoming addicted to cigarettes.

Two of my great-grandparents have died from lung cancer. They were both also lifelong smokers. Two generations later and their children are still smoking. My great-grandparents smoked their entire lives, and both died of lung cancer. Some people may think the younger generations who continue to smoke, like my grandparents, parents, and cousins, should learn from my great-grandparents' mistake. But it's not that simple. I encourage those people who think smoking is a dumb Kentuckian mistake to look at families like mine with more compassion and understanding.

REFERENCES

1. "Smoking and Tobacco Use: Health Effects of Secondhand Smoke," Centers for Disease Control and Prevention, 2020, https://www.cdc.

gov/tobacco/data_statistics/fact_sheets/secondhand_smoke/health_ effects/index.htm.

2. "The Science of Drug Use and Addiction: The Basics," National Institute on Drug Abuse, 2021, https://www.drugabuse.gov/publications/ media-guide/science-drug-use-addiction-basics.

3. A. Felman, "Everything You Need to Know about Nicotine," Medical News Today, updated January 11, 2018, https://www.medicalnewstoday.com/articles/240820#_noHeaderPrefixedContent.

4. N. L. Benowitz, "Pharmacology of Nicotine: Addiction, Smoking-Induced Disease, and Therapeutics," *Annual Review of Pharmacology and Toxicology* 49 (2009): 57–71.

5. "Smoking & Tobacco Use: Health Effects of Cigarette Smoking," Centers for Disease Control and Prevention, 2021, https://www.cdc.gov/tobacco/data_statistics/fact_sheets/health_effects/effects_cig_ smoking/index.htm.

6. "Side Effects of Eating Too Much Chocolate," Santosham Crest Hospital, 2018, http://www.sanchest.com/side-effects-of-eating-too-much-chocolate.html.

7. J. Kuroski, "33 Vintage Cigarette Ads That Are Now Hilariously, Tragically Absurd," All That's Interesting, June 24, 2016, https://allthatsinteresting.com/vintage-cigarette-ads.

8. A. Glass, "Congress Bans Airing Cigarette Ads, April 1, 1970." *Politico*, April 1, 2018, https://www.politico.com/story/2018/04/01/ congress-bans-airing-cigarette-ads-april-1-1970-489882.

9. National Center for Chronic Disease Prevention and Health Promotion (US) Office on Smoking and Health, "Fifty Years of Change 1964–2014," in *The Health Consequences of Smoking—50 Years of Progress: A Report of the Surgeon General* (Atlanta, GA: Centers for Disease Control and Prevention, 2014), https://www.ncbi.nlm.nih.gov/books/ NBK294310/.

10. "BRFSS Prevalence & Trends Data," Centers for Disease Control and Prevention, n.d., https://nccd.cdc.gov/brfssprevalence/rdPage. aspx/rdPage.aspx?rdReport=DPH_BRFSS.ExploreByLocation&isl-Location=99&go=GO.

11. "Tobacco Use in Kentucky 2019," Truth Initiative, 2019, https://truthinitiative.org/research-resources/smoking-region/tobacco-use-kentucky-2019.

12. "Smoking & Tobacco Use: Health Effects," Centers for Disease Control and Prevention, 2021, https://www.cdc.gov/tobacco/basic_information/health_effects/index.htm.

13. "Kentucky: Key Health Indicators," Centers for Disease Control and Prevention, 2021, https://www.cdc.gov/nchs/pressroom/states/kentucky/ky.htm.

14. "Stats of the States: Cancer Mortality," Centers for Disease Control and Prevention, accessed November 17, 2020, https://www.cdc.gov/nchs/pressroom/sosmap/cancer_mortality/cancer.htm.

15. "Burden of Lung Cancer Pushes Kentucky's Cancer Rate to Nation's Highest," *USA Today*, December 22, 2015, https://www.usatoday.com/story/news/nation/2015/12/22/burden-lung-cancer-pushes-kentuckys-cancer-rates-nations-highest/77742740/.

A CONTINUOUS WAR: CANCER IN KENTUCKY

Michael Buoncristiani

I was born and raised in Wayne County, Kentucky. History reveals that my county was named after a Revolutionary War hero by the name of "Mad" Anthony Wayne [1]. Since then, another war has come into the hands of not only my community but also nearly all the surrounding counties in most of the Appalachian region. This is a war that won't be won because of the shot of a gun or the wave of a flag. No, it will be won through the uniting of communities and people from across the world. This is a war that has taken countless valuable lives of many loved ones, friends, and young children. It is a war against a great foe that is all too familiar to many: cancer. Cancer in the United States is estimated to take the lives of over 600,000 people we love in 2021 [2].

Nearly everyone in Appalachia has personal experience with cancer, and my closest experiences have come through my grandfathers. Their cancer cases were diagnosed when I was very young, so I did not understand much about the situation at the time. I did, however, understand the pain cancer brought to all members of my family, and I could feel the emotion. One of them is still having a bout with his cancer. A leiomyosarcoma, which started in his leg many years ago, metastasized to the lungs, and this began a long-term relationship of nearly 15 years with the Markey Cancer Center.

I have seen firsthand what having a close family member with cancer is like. Even as a small child, I was able to understand the toll that it took on the family around me; although, I was somewhat "shielded" from all of it, I would say. As I have grown older, I understand more of what is going on, and it has helped me be able to notice and empathize with the pain of others around me in these tough situations.

Many in my area also have loved ones who are diagnosed with cancer due to its high prevalence in Eastern Kentucky. To understand why cancer rates are so high, we can look at an introduction to cancer and what it is. As cancer researcher Ludmil Alexandrov wrote:

> "All cancers originate from a single cell that starts to behave abnormally, to divide uncontrollably, and, eventually, to invade adjacent tissues." [3]

The abnormal behavior of the single cell is due to changes in the DNA or mutations. These changes can be caused by exposure to different mutagens and other mechanisms. The often-small changes found in cancers are related to causes such as smoking [3].

According to the Centers for Disease Control and Prevention (CDC), Kentucky has had around 10,000 cancer deaths every year for the past decade [4]. These rates have been higher than any other state, year after year. Cancer is everywhere in our state, and many factors contribute to the statistics our cancer rates produce every year. In my own community, I see many reasons why cancer is prevalent in our area.

First, the rates of obesity in Appalachia are significantly higher than anywhere else in the United States [5]. In particular, the "Adult Obesity Prevalence Maps" show that the two states that have obesity rates of 35 percent or higher are Kentucky and West Virginia. Interestingly, both of these states are located in the Appalachian region, which is swamped with cancer incidence and fatalities.

There are very high cancer risks involved with obesity. A study shows that obesity is linked to a higher risk of cancers, including colorectal, liver, breast, pancreatic, and many more [6]. Obesity is a problem that you see in nearly every area of the community, but it is a problem that can be overcome with outreach, education, and action.

The obesity rates we see are related to two areas of life: nutrition and exercise. In a state-reported survey, local health departments reported that Kentucky had at least 30 percent of residents that are physically inactive [7]. The statements were based on this question: "During the past month, other than your regular job, did you participate in any physical activities or exercise such as running, calisthenics, golf, gardening or walking for exercise?" [7] Respondents were classified as physically inactive if they responded "no." One limitation of these findings is that the study used phone interviews and self-reported statements, which makes it difficult to ascertain its accuracy.

In my community, eating well is not very common. Poor eating habits are a direct line to obesity. In many cases, it can be cheaper and significantly easier to eat poorly. However, these cannot be used as an excuse for us to continue to participate in bad lifestyle habits. There are many cases in which people may not know the importance of healthy eating and the positive effects that it can make in their lives, not only with respect to cancer and obesity but also in almost every aspect of their daily lives.

Education is one of the most important parts of our lives. The phrase "knowledge is power" may be cliché, but it is very true. I believe that the low education rates with regard to cancer and health in small communities in Appalachia are the primary explanation of the high incidence rates. The understanding of cancer in communities such as mine is very low. This could be caused by multiple factors, including limited outreach and a lack of resources. A community that has more healthcare providers would be more likely to have increased screenings, higher education, and additional preventive measures. However, this is a feat that cannot be achieved in one day. Outreach to tap into the educational side of cancer would help ignite the flame. Many people who are diagnosed with cancer do not know that there are treatment options and facilities that are paving the way in oncology around them. In an area that is underserved, there may not be a treatment center right down the road. In my community there are no oncologists, and one of the closest cancer centers is the Markey Cancer Center at the University of Kentucky, which is roughly two hours away. Increasing the number of cancer care facilities would lead to more patients being able to achieve a positive cancer treatment outcome without having to make the long trip.

Finally, there is one other factor that contributes greatly to cancer statistics in my hometown: tobacco. In my community, there are high rates of cigarette smoking. The CDC maps show that some of the highest percentages of smoking residents live in Kentucky and West Virginia [8]. Tobacco use and smoking are not something to be overlooked. Smoking consistently accounts for 80 percent of all lung cancer deaths, and it increases one's risk of developing other cancers and health problems. Along with an increased risk of many cancers, smoking also "worsens cancer outcomes" [9].

Now that we have established smoking's negative health effects, we must consider possible solutions. I love my community of Wayne County; I want to see the community and the families in it be healthy and happy. I know that the cancer crisis in my community is big, but the solution is bigger. The solution will be the result of not only community change but also change everywhere. People are aware of the high cancer rates in Appalachia and have been for many years. There are many solutions, but I believe the following few will make a great impact in my community: outreach for education, more programs in place to provide care for cancer patients, and assistance for those in need of treatment. These are just the beginning of the solution.

These types of outreach programs have been funded to decrease rates in Appalachian cancer for years. In fact, the NCI started doing cancer outreach in Appalachia as early as 1986 [10]. With this pioneer program, there were some failures, but much was learned. The NCI found that outreach was most effective when leaders of the area were involved, giving a sense of community to the effort [10]. Furthermore, this has proven to be very effective in our communities.

Outreach will involve much more than just teaching others what cancer is. It needs to include education on cancer treatments, promising outcomes, and additional services provided by cancer centers. Markey Cancer Center has many available resources to help patients have the best experience possible while going through their treatments. Many people do not know of additional resources such as the American Cancer Society's Hope Lodge, an organization that provides overnight stays at no cost for patients receiving treatment.

Also, outreach needs to promote positive habits as well as the necessary education of cancer and options for those with cancer. Preventive cancer education should be brought to school systems. The outcomes for children in the long run would improve if teachers taught about cancer throughout their educational careers. This would involve more than a school promoting a guest speaker; we need the help of all staff in the schools of our communities to come together for the fight. In our science classes, more coverage of the disease and its prevention, even if on only topical bases, would be a huge win against cancer. Teachers should cover not only what cancer is and the preventive measures, but they also should discuss why preventive habits are so important.

In many cases, people need to see how behavioral changes can affect their lives so greatly. People need to be exposed to education about cancer so they can understand how they need to change. There are many people that do not want to change what they do, and that's human nature. Maybe they just need an extra push, a reason why. Together, we may be able to provide this push that is needed to save countless lives of friends and family members around us. The effects of cancer on communities and families are devastating, and we need to take action now.

REFERENCES

1. H. Ogle, *Deep Roots and Rich History: Historical Glimpses of Monticello and Wayne County, Kentucky* (Madison, MS: Morris Publishing, 2002).

2. R. L. Siegel et al., "Cancer Statistics, 2021," *CA: A Cancer Journal for Clinicians* 71, no. 1 (January–February 2021): 7–33, https://acsjournals.onlinelibrary.wiley.com/doi/10.3322/caac.21654.

3. L. B. Alexandrov, "Understanding the Origins of Human Cancer," *Science* 350, no. 6265 (2015): 1175, https://www.science.org/doi/10.1126/science.aad7363?url_ver=Z39.88-2003&rfr_id=ori%3Arid%3Across-ref.org&rfr_dat=cr_pub++0pubmed&.

4. "Stats of the States: Cancer Mortality," Centers for Disease Control

and Prevention, accessed November 17, 2020, https://www.cdc.gov/nchs/pressroom/sosmap/cancer_mortality/cancer.htm.

5. "Adult Obesity Prevalence Maps," Centers for Disease Control and Prevention, 2021, https://www.cdc.gov/obesity/data/prevalence-maps.html.

6. T. Pischon and K. Nimptsch, eds., *Obesity and Cancer* (New York: Springer International Publishing, 2016).

7. "Adult Physical Inactivity Prevalence Maps by Race/Ethnicity," Centers for Disease Control and Prevention, 2020, www.cdc.gov/physicalactivity/data/inactivity-prevalence-maps/.

8. "Map of Cigarette Use among Adults," Centers for Disease Control and Prevention, 2018, www.cdc.gov/statesystem/cigaretteuseadult.html.

9. M. Patlak and E. Balogh, eds., *Reducing Tobacco-Related Cancer Incidence and Mortality: Workshop Summary, Institute of Medicine, Board on Health Care Services, and National Cancer Policy Forum* (Washington, DC: National Academics Press, 2013).

10. R. A. Couto, *Sowing Seeds in the Mountains: Community-Based Coalitions for Cancer Prevention and Control* (London: Forgotten Books, 2019).

THE BATTLE AGAINST CANCER

Alexander Chang

People want a healthy, cancer-free life for themselves, their families and friends. Despite this, I observe many Eastern Kentuckians struggle to maintain a consistent level of physical activity and a balanced diet. When I visit other areas of the United States, I notice that my rural community does not have similar opportunities that other cities have to benefit their health. However, the media promote that those who engage in a weekly exercise regimen, along with proper nutrition and diet, will decrease their chance of developing cancer. We need to do work now to eliminate cancer-causing factors in rural Appalachia's impoverished communities. In order to advance the fight to beat cancer, continued education and awareness are essential to destroying carcinogenic disease in Eastern Kentucky.

After high school, I wanted to branch out of my small, tight-knit community in Pikeville, Kentucky. I wanted to experience another demographic region and culture and still reside in my home state. I decided to further my college education in Lexington. I study human nutrition at the University of Kentucky and am developing a strong understanding of how the body functions and processes nutrients for everyday tasks. I am learning the advantage of choosing a healthier food group over a tasty, greasy, unhealthy snack.

Nutritional balance is an essential component of any health program. In my studies I learn food choices are an essential consideration in maintaining healthy nutrition habits before and during cancer therapy to keep the body healthy and the mind positive. Understanding nutritional information gives me the perspective as a volunteer with the Bluegrass Hospice Care Center at UK Albert B. Chandler Hospital, where I interact with patients whose systems are frail due to cancer.

My goal is to become a physician and give back to my rural community. I intend to provide a holistic approach to medicine, ensuring not only the health of the patients but also their well-being. Along with the support and mentorship of the Appalachian Career Training in Oncology (ACTION) Program, I will gain a scientific understanding of cancer at the cellular level. I will learn from healthcare professionals and researchers searching for answers to combat cancer. Hopefully, these lessons and experiences will grant me the opportunity to give back to my community one day and continue the uphill battle in the fight to terminate cancer in Eastern Kentucky.

Smoking cigarettes is a hard habit to break. I see smokers in my community, and I wonder how many people will be impacted by lung cancer in Eastern Kentucky. Routines and patterns start at home. Children and young adults are more likely to mirror parents' actions and therefore are at a higher risk of developing bad habits from their parents. I remember a classmate telling me that he was intrigued when his grandmother would ask him to light her cigarette. He admitted that he enjoyed the smell of the tobacco and found it striking how the cigarette paper burned away. We must educate our young people in the state of Kentucky, and more cancer education is needed to discourage the mimicking of smoking and bring awareness to this crisis.

Conversations of the negative effects cigarette smoking causes and avoidance of tobacco products need to be discussed with children and young adults. I understand why my mother was against cigarette smoking in our home; she wanted to instill a healthy environment for her children. All family members and friends were aware of this rule when they came to visit. As an asthmatic child, I was not allowed to play with candy cigarettes, although I did when my mother was busy. The fake smoking substance had a red stain at the stump, giving the impression of a lit cigarette, so in turn, I would deeply inhale. Even with my mother's rule, I would find time to sneak away with my 10-year-old friend and pretend to blow the sweet-tasting smoke from my mouth. Frequently, children are susceptible to mischievous actions and deliberately break the rules. A preventive measure is not to start smoking in the home.

My late great-grandpa, Andres, was a chronic smoker, and the odor of the tobacco lingered on his clothes. The discoloration of his teeth was apparent by years of cigarette smoking. His silver, wavy hair was cut every three weeks by a barber who smoked. Most of my great-grandpa's friends were smokers. Andres was a businessman, and he interacted with the public. He tried to quit smoking many times. His method was to suck on a piece of menthol candy or eat continuously throughout the day to suppress his insatiable craving. He always needed to have an oral fixation in order to get through the day, and soon he began to gain weight. Due to this uncontrollable desire, he also began having trouble getting around and soon started to have difficulty breathing. His cough was loud, and soon his handkerchief became a dingy yellowish-red caused by the thick secretions he coughed up into it. He refused to go to the doctor (most likely he did not want his poor prognosis validated), and soon he never went anywhere at all. He stopped visiting his barber and had my great-grandma cut his hair. He started wearing only his pajamas around the house. As his appetite diminished severely, he refused food and liquids. He lost weight. He was always cold and often stayed in his bed, curled up with a few blankets on him. He hardly spoke because he was so short of breath. He would cough so much that my great-grandma would close the bedroom door and sleep restlessly on the couch. The pattern of interrupted sleep persisted for two months; then one morning she listened, only silence. My great-grandma found him on the bed with a large pool of blood on the pillow. At 48 years old, my great-grandpa died of lung cancer. In all the days of his life, the word "cancer" never was brought up.

Pikeville is affected by more than just lung cancer; we are affected by breast cancer as well. Paint Pikeville Pink (PPP) is an annual 5K race/one-mile fun walk to raise proceeds for Blessed Beyond Measure, a nonprofit charity that aims to help impoverished and uninsured cancer patients in Eastern Kentucky. Surrounding communities are encouraged to join the city of Pikeville to learn about breast cancer prevention while giving survivors a chance to share their own emotional battles. This venue raises funds to obtain resources for the disadvantaged in the community and encourages people to have timely breast screenings. The key to assessing this disease is early detection, followed by an immediate treatment plan.

The PPP fundraiser increases breast cancer awareness and aims to decrease the severe financial strain on Eastern Kentucky's impoverished citizens. Volunteers are on hand at this event to form a connection with people needing assistance and are also available to help initiate the first steps in scheduling a mammogram appointment. Information and education afford options to people impacted by their struggling socioeconomic status in Eastern Kentucky, resulting in hope for a healthy lifestyle and a decrease in the breast cancer rate.

The one-day breast cancer charity event offers financial education awareness to underinsured and uninsured citizens. PPP is an
avenue in my rural town where people in local communities come
together and raise funds for those lacking resources. Medical costs
are devastating, and the bills pile up. People who do not have the
cash may ignore a breast cancer checkup. The resources from this
event help finance breast cancer screening for those who lack the
money to pay medical bills.

PPP celebrates National Breast Cancer Awareness Month
on a scheduled Saturday in October. The event has grown since
2011, and at times more than 700 participants have filled their
applications for this benefit. The pink decorations and pink rib-
bons symbolize breast cancer awareness. The participants unite in
wearing this symbolic color.

Pink is the cancer awareness color. At PPP people dress in
different assortments of pink fashion; and of course, a friendly,
pink-painted poodle barks at the finish line. People are running and
walking while talking and laughing. One can see pink-decorated
strollers and babies, young children in pink T-shirts, and older
adults wearing pink tutus, all coming together to participate in
this breast cancer cause. This environment is a significant step in
the right direction; people must place their health as the highest of
priorities. If we can instill the belief that the community members
are here to support each other, it is possible to increase breast
cancer awareness through family and friends.

Two years ago, I met a woman at PPP who had been diagnosed
with breast cancer in December of 2011 and also had a niece who
had been diagnosed with breast cancer. The niece lived with the
disease for two years before she passed away at the age of 32.
The woman I met said everyone's journey with cancer is different.
In her case, she received several breast biopsies and a magnetic
resonance imaging (MRI) scan before her physician concluded

that she had breast cancer. At first, the doctors said a lumpectomy with a complete nipple removal was advised, which would solve the issue, but she had more questions. She wanted to be educated and comfortable with her decision. She was introduced to someone at the Lexington Clinic who happened to be a breast care coordinator. During this meeting, she was able to discuss options with someone other than a medical provider. She decided to have a double mastectomy because she did not want to stress about breast cancer ever again. She had the surgery and soon began the next phase of her recovery, starting four chemotherapy rounds. Eventually, she had the final operation to place her permanent breast implants. The woman who shared her story with me has been breast cancer free since her surgery and treatments.

Education and prevention are the keys to beating cancer. I study that the food we eat can increase our chance in the prevention of cancer. Children playing with candy cigarettes as I did are at risk to become smokers. My great-grandpa, Andres, a loving man with an unhealthy habit, felt shame and did not seek help early. Healthy food habits can counter this tobacco influence. Choosing a healthier diet would include the inclusion of lean meats, beans, and other plant-based foods while limiting the amount of processed foods and meats like lamb, pork, and beef. The devastation caused by cancer harms entire families and neighborhoods. It is essential to maintain proper nutrition and healthy eating habits to have a positive domino effect on one's body and attitude. Nutrition fuels the body, and poor choices make it harder to be active, so it's not as simple as one or the other but a joint effort to change habits. A goal of mine is to become a medical doctor and return home to educate my community on the benefits of food choices.

In addition to diet, Kentuckians need to incorporate physical activity into their weekly schedules to decrease the chance of contracting cancer. Exercise can increase metabolism and reduce the harmful effects of inactivity by improving overall fitness. A benefit to our health is changing our habits. For example, climbing the stairs over standing in the elevator can add to feeling mentally sharp and physically fit. We need to remind ourselves in our rural communities to push forward and increase our physical activity to lower the risk of cancer.

The community that is dear to my heart can only gain by making cancer confrontation an urgent priority by incorporating preventive methods. The first step in recognizing the fight to battle cancer is early detection. A healthy, cancer-free society for the current community and the generations to follow is of utmost importance. The people in rural communities are resilient and supportive. We must help ourselves by focusing on regular check-ups and cancer-screening appointments throughout the year and follow a sensible diet and exercise to help us in preventing cancer in Eastern Kentucky.

FIGHTING AGAINST UNBRIDLED CANCER IN KENTUCKY

Tyra Gilbert

There is a reason someone wrote a song called "My Old Kentucky Home." Most people associate Kentucky with fried chicken, college basketball, bluegrass, horses, family and mountains, and they would be correct! My home state has many great aspects and features that most Kentuckians are proud of. However, there is something else that the state of Kentucky has more of than any state in the US, a title that I do not think any state wants. Kentucky holds the title of having the highest cancer incidence and mortality rates in the US [1]. The statistics that give us this title are not just numbers. They are real people with families and lives that are totally disrupted. There is absolutely a crisis occurring in Kentucky, a cancer crisis.

My name is Tyra Gilbert, and I was raised in Leslie County, Kentucky. In Leslie County there is a small and humble city named Hyden. It is a place with a total of two stoplights, one high school, and three fast-food restaurants. However, what we lack in streets and avenues, we make up in beautiful mountains and country roads. When I was a kid, everywhere I looked there would be a mountain somewhere in view, and I liked to imagine they were hugging my county. Now that I am older, I think my younger self was on to something. No matter how many times I leave my town or visit different places, coming back always gives me the same feeling that you feel when you receive a hug: a feeling of love and safety, something like home. This feeling resonates with the people who live in Appalachia too, as it is something you can feel from them in the way they cook, act, and speak.

The people of Appalachia have experiences unlike anywhere else, but the experiences are not always good. The people who live in my county, like those that live in most of the counties in Appalachia, experience many struggles. Some of these struggles are socioeconomic difficulties like low-income households, unemployment, and low rates of achieving higher education. Substance abuse and limited access to healthcare are also large problems in Kentucky. These difficulties certainly show themselves in the health problems that people in Appalachia are now experiencing. For example, Kentucky has high rates of heart disease, obesity, and cancer when compared to the national average [1, 2]. Though all of these are harmful, it seems that cancer is the most established disease that affects more people than you could imagine.

Since I can remember, cancer has always played a huge role in my community and life. It affected me before I was even born. My mother was taken in by her foster family when she was a teenager, but her foster dad had gotten lung cancer. This cancer led to his death and took him away before I could meet him. My family still talks about the man he was to this day; he will always be missed by them. My next experience with cancer was with one of my closest friends, whose father was diagnosed with cancer. I watched and helped her family take care of him. All the while, he suffered through the disease. He later passed away because of his cancer, leaving his family behind. The pain I saw them experience was something too many people have to go through in Kentucky. My other close friend was also affected when her mother, someone who was like a second mom to me, was diagnosed with breast cancer. I watched my friend and her family endure the fear of not knowing whether her mother would live or die. This fear, pain, and loss from cancer is something that many Kentuckians experience far too often.

Seeing all the effects of cancer on my community really got me interested in the "why" of the situation. I wondered why people weren't surprised or shocked when they learned that a friend or distant family had cancer. I wondered why they were not stunned or astonished, just simply disappointed. It is as if people just heard "someone has cancer" so much, they weren't shocked by the news of it anymore. I also wondered why Kentucky has the most cancer cases and mortality in the US. These "whys" are what lead me to my career path today. It has been my desire to become a medical doctor since I was a kid, and that is what I came to college for. My curiosity about cancer made me want to know more about the disease and how I could help with what I was studying. I wanted to become someone who could give back to my area and help in some way.

At the end of my freshman year of college, it was obvious to me that I wanted to pursue a medical degree. It was not long after that I learned of the Appalachian Career Training in Oncology (ACTION) Program. This program seemed perfect for me, so I applied and was accepted! The ACTION program has been—and continues to be—a program that has opened up many opportunities for myself and others. ACTION provided me an opportunity to join a research lab here at the University of Kentucky that focuses on toxicology and cancer biology in the lungs. My experience in the lab gave me a new outlook on how research works and the effort that is put into it. With this experience, I learned that I do not want to pursue mainly research as a career. That said, I do hope to become a doctor who works in collaboration with researchers. I would like to become a doctor who works with others to help solve the cancer problem in Kentucky.

From my experience, I think miseducation is a large contributor to the high cancer rates in Kentucky. Most people do not take into consideration how their lifestyle can so heavily affect them. Factors such as tobacco smoking, tobacco chewing, alcohol abuse, and UV rays are things that lead to cancer, which most people do not take into account. Their preexisting diseases such as diabetes can also be a factor in their susceptibility to cancer [3], something that is not widely known in my hometown. There need to be more educational programs and presentations to help inform people about how the things in their lifestyle affect their health and how to change them.

Two problems that are very prevalent in Kentucky and pave a way for cancer are inadequate healthcare and funding. Kentucky has a much higher cancer rate when compared to the national average [1]. People who have other diseases like diabetes usually have lifestyles that, along with their conditions, increase their chances of getting cancer [3]. I think better healthcare, healthcare programs, and outreach can significantly help with these problems that are taking over in Kentucky, including cancer. Everyone does not have the same problems and lifestyles, so a variety of programs and outreach can help this. I think there should also be more specialty doctors to, among other things, help people in the Appalachian region with healthier lifestyle choices (such as eating healthier foods and exercising). Healthier lifestyles and healthier people can decrease chances of developing cancer and increase chances of survival if diagnosed [4].

Cancer has taken too many people. It has caused too much pain, loss, fear, and confusion. There is a crisis in Kentucky and specifically in Appalachia. However, this is not a fight I think we should lose, nor is it a title I think we should hold. It is up to us to fight back against this disease, to help take care of our own and each other. This crisis may have us down now, but I do not think it can keep us down. We are a lively people with an unbridled spirit, and as the Kentucky website states:

> "Kentucky is a place where spirits are free to soar, and big dreams can be fulfilled. We relish competition and cherish our champions for their willingness to push beyond conventional boundaries to reach new heights of success." [5]

Together and not divided, Kentuckians can overcome the cancer crisis that has afflicted our people for far too long.

REFERENCES

1. "Stats of the States: Cancer Mortality," Centers for Disease Control and Prevention, accessed November 17, 2020, https://www.cdc.gov/nchs/pressroom/sosmap/cancer_mortality/cancer.htm.

2. "National Environmental Public Health Tracking," Centers for Disease Control and Prevention, 2020, https://www.cdc.gov/nceh/tracking/profiles/Kentucky_Profile.htm.

3. K. K. Collins, "The Diabetes-Cancer Link," *Diabetes Spectrum* 27, no. 4 (2014): 276–280, https://www.ncbi.nlm.nih.gov/pmc/articles/PMC4231938/.

4. "Diet and Physical Activity: What's the Cancer Connection?" American Cancer Society, 2021, https://www.cancer.org/cancer/cancer-causes/diet-physical-activity/diet-and-physical-activity.html.

5. "Kentucky Unbridled Spirit," Kentucky.gov, 2021, https://kentucky.gov/about/pages/unbridledspirit.aspx.

GETTING A FIGHTING CHANCE

Abby Hill

My name is Abby Hill, and I'm a freshman at the University of Kentucky. I'm studying biology and hope to go to medical school after college to be a plastic surgeon or gastroenterologist. I'm from Richmond, Kentucky, which is on the western border of the Appalachian region. Growing up, I never really considered myself to be from Appalachia. I don't face many of the hardships that people growing up deep in Appalachia do, so I didn't realize that many of the problems that are prevalent further east are also present in my hometown. I didn't realize that even though poverty isn't running rampant in Richmond, people still struggle to pay medical bills. I didn't realize that my own family members lack access to healthcare while battling cancer. I didn't realize that feeling like cancer is just a common part of life isn't normal.

Cancer is a major health crisis affecting Appalachia more than it does the rest of the United States. High rates of poverty and poor health practices in the region contribute to the development of cancer, and the lack of access to healthcare keeps people from recovering. To combat this disease, we need to educate youth so they can be advocates for their homes. We also need to increase telemedicine and at-home treatments so the healthcare people need can be close to home.

All of Appalachia suffers from the effects of cancer, but one of the worst-hit communities is Owsley County, Kentucky. Owsley County is my mother's hometown and home to much of my extended family. I have spent a lot of my time there with family, and the community is special to me; it breaks my heart to see them suffer the way they do. It is no coincidence that of my grandmother's five siblings, three have had cancer. One sister passed away from breast cancer a few years ago. The other sister had rectal cancer and went through radiation and chemotherapy and had part of her colon removed. She now lives with a colostomy bag and a weakened body and immune system. She also lives with the fear that her cancer will return, but she can't have colonoscopies or other checkups because her colon was burned so badly from the radiation. The oldest brother is currently receiving treatment for prostate cancer. Their father had prostate cancer many years ago.

Even if living in Appalachia didn't cause their cancer, it certainly didn't make their time with it any easier. It feels like everywhere I look, someone else is suffering from cancer. Every week at church people ask for prayers for a loved one as they go to the doctor for diagnosis or surgery. I didn't even realize how many people in my family had gone through something with cancer until I asked my parents so that I could write this essay. Even on the outskirts of Appalachia, cancer is hurting so many people and communities. I am fortunate to have not lost anyone close to me to cancer, but I am in the minority. We have to work together to educate ourselves on why this is such a problem and what we can do to make a change. We can't just accept cancer as something that just happens to people. It doesn't have to happen to our families and our friends; and, if it does, we need to be prepared to help them get the care they need and deserve. To make a change we have to first understand what is causing the problem in the first place.

One of the major factors contributing to the cancer crisis in Appalachia is the economy, because it creates a stressful environment for those living there and leaves people unable to afford care. The Appalachian economy used to run on coal and tobacco farming, but both of those industries are dying. Their fall has hurt the economy and caused poverty to run rampant. Owsley County has some of the worst employment rates out of all the Appalachian counties, with 9.6 percent of people without jobs and a median income of only $21,000 [1]. With this extreme economic hardship comes stress and depression, and people often turn to food, alcohol, and cigarettes to cope with their pain. Forty-two percent of adults in Owsley County smoke, compared with 26 percent in Kentucky and only 15 percent nationwide [1]. Cigarette smoke is a well-known cancer-causing agent, increasing a person's odds of developing lung cancer as much as 14 times that of a nonsmoker [1], but in an environment where so many people smoke, it isn't seen for the problem that it is [2]. Cigarettes affect the health of nonsmokers as well because of the potentially deadly effects of secondhand smoke.

Over 34 percent of Kentucky adults are obese, nearly 70 percent are overweight [1], and excess weight with lack of physical activity are major contributors to cancer. People in this region don't have the extra time or money to spend on going to the gym and eating the healthiest food. Health constantly falls to the side as caring for families and making some sustainable income are at the forefront of people's minds. These health factors greatly increase the cancer rates in Appalachia, but the overall attitude of the people living there also contributes to the problem.

Most Appalachians have worked tirelessly for what little they have, and they value their independence and work ethic. This means many don't appreciate the sometimes patronizing approach that outsiders take to providing aid. As Phillip Obermiller says, many outsiders see the Appalachian culture as one of dysfunction and see it as "diseased" [3]. People don't take kindly to being seen as inferior, especially in a culture that takes such pride in its self-reliance, so this type of approach to helping the region could make many people reluctant to accept assistance.

Another prominent value is self-sacrifice for the sake of caring for your loved ones. In my own family I have seen this selflessness drive many to unnecessary sickness. While he didn't have cancer, the example of my uncle's heart attack perfectly illustrates this concept. He had a heart attack that nearly killed him, and he still struggles with dangerously low blood pressure, but he refuses to stop working on the farm because he doesn't want to ask for or accept help. This type of attitude prevents people from getting cancer care. They don't want to be a financial burden on their families or to take up their time to drive them to the doctor. Despite their elevated risks for the disease, countless Appalachians refuse to get treatment or even be screened because they don't want to be burdens to their families.

While this region sees significantly more diagnoses of cancer, they have significantly less access to treatment and care. The small, scattered populations of this region can't support large grocery stores, let alone hospitals that can provide diverse and comprehensive care. The drive from Owsley County to the Markey Cancer Center in Lexington takes nearly two hours, and people simply don't have the time to make the trip as often as is needed to appropriately treat their cancers. Even if they had time to make the long journeys to a hospital, many in this poverty-stricken region don't have health insurance or savings to cover the cost of treatment.

Even larger cities like Richmond, Kentucky, don't have the

facilities to treat many types of cancer. My grandfather has been having treatment for skin cancer, and he has to drive about an hour to Lexington for treatment five days a week. He was a mailman for years and never wore sunscreen, and the sun damaged his skin. Now, he's had nearly 20 excisional surgeries to remove cancerous places on his skin, and he has to wear protective clothing to go outside. He has to shape his day around driving to get treatment; and, on days where he has surgery, he is usually at the hospital the entire day. I can only imagine how much worse it would be if he lived even farther away from his treatment.

Another woman that went to my church passed away from breast cancer about 10 years ago. She is probably the first person I really remember having cancer. She had to travel out of state for many of her treatments. This must have put serious financial stress on her family as well as emotional stress from hours on the road and weeks away from home. Nobody wants to be far from home when they're sick, so having to travel constantly for treatment can only worsen an already terrible experience.

Because of this lack of access to treatment, many people don't even get screened for cancer. According to Carrie Arnold in "Appalachia's Cancer Problem" [2], fewer than one in ten women in Appalachia is properly screened for breast, cervical, or colorectal cancer, which are all very treatable when detected early. People simply lack hope: Many don't see any point in screening, because they can't afford treatment anyway or they don't have time to make the long journey to the doctor. They would rather let cancer kill them without them knowing than to start a battle they don't feel like they can finish. Many changes need to be made to how we deal with cancer in Appalachia so that people can feel like they have a chance to heal from the disease.

One way to help people diagnosed with cancer is to bring the care to them. While many treatments and preventive care measures must be done in a hospital setting, there are other parts of cancer care that can be made accessible to people in their own homes. For example, increasing the use of telemedicine, which allows people to use apps to track their symptoms and speak to doctors and nurses, reduces the need for in-person checkups. We should increase research on ways to make treatments that can be home-based so that patients aren't having to disrupt their lives to travel to hospitals.

Another area that needs improvement is access to screening and screening education. Many types of screenings can be done in mobile screening vans. Increasing these mobile screenings, as well as educating people on the importance of getting screened, could help more people detect their cancers early and survive. The mobile screenings need to be heavily advertised so people are aware of the opportunity and can take advantage of it.

Probably the most important thing we can do is educate and involve Appalachia's youth. I didn't learn about the high cancer rates in Appalachia until I was a senior in high school applying for the Appalachian Career Training in Oncology (ACTION) Program. If more young people know and care about the cancer problem, we will have more people able to go into our communities and make the changes we need. People from outside our region don't understand its people and their lives. We need people who have grown up here and have a passion for making changes to make their communities healthier at the forefront of these changes.

We can't live in fear and hopelessness and let cancer keep taking our health and the health of those we love. It will take a long time, and it won't be easy, but we have to continue to make progress until Appalachians have a fair chance against cancer. Nobody should feel like they don't have the option to fight for their health. These people are fighters. They fight every day just to feed their families and to keep their lights on. They fight for their education when it isn't readily available. They fight for health when their environment makes it so difficult. If they could, these people would fight cancer too, and they would probably win, but as of right now, they don't have that opportunity simply because they live in the Appalachian Mountains. That is unfair and we have to change it.

REFERENCES

1. L. Gilpin, "Cancer Rates Are Dropping—But Not in Rural Appalachia," FiveThirtyEight, February 14, 2017, https://fivethirtyeight. com/features/cancer-rates-are-dropping-but-not-in-rural-appalachia/.

2. C. Arnold, "Appalachia's Cancer Problem," *JNCI: Journal of the National Cancer Institute* 109, no. 3 (2017), https://academic.oup.com/ jnci/article/109/3/djx045/3073434.

3. P. J. Obermiller and M. E. Maloney, "The Uses and Misuses of Appalachian Culture," *Journal of Appalachian Studies* 22, no. 1 (2016): 103–112, https://www.uacvoice.org/docs/researcharchive/workingpapers/workingpaper20.pdf.

KENTUCKY'S CANCER BURDEN: FROM FEARFUL AND UNINFORMED TO TAKING ACTION

Caroline Jenkins

I have lived in Kentucky my whole life. It's a place where my father, my grandfather, and his parents grew up. We make up generations of Kentuckians. I grew up in Mount Sterling, a small town in Eastern Kentucky. It was a life of living out in the country while still being about seven minutes from town, a town where I know nearly everyone. I remember a lot about living there—sitting on the porch with my mom, celebrating Christmas with my grandparents, playing in the backyard in the summer, sledding on the rolling hills in the winter, hiking with my dad, and so much more.

Although my small town has given me a lot, it also left me with a lot of questions. I did not know much about anything outside of Mount Sterling, much less about the community around me. That is, until I went to college. I attended the University of Kentucky (UK) in Lexington. Here, I lived a life full of studying, meeting new people, and exploring this new place, all in the hopes of one day attending medical school. The rumors are true; you really do feel like a small fish in a big pond when you move from a small city to a large one. During my time at UK, I've learned so much about the diversity of Kentucky and its culture. As I learned, I began to feel completely overwhelmed with how blind I had been to the hardships and disparities that Kentucky faces, one of which is cancer.

Cancer was not always a part of my life—at least, not a big part. I felt very sheltered from most of life's challenges, right up until my grandpa was diagnosed with bile duct cancer in 2008. Bile duct cancer is a very rare cancer and goes pretty much undetected until it has reached stage four. I can remember the last family vacation we had before he was sick. Every summer, we traveled to Michigan to live in a big cabin with my grandparents and my cousins. I've made some of my best memories there. I remember that last summer well. It had all the good memories, swimming in the lake, catching frogs, playing board games, but one thing was new. My grandpa was sick; it started with jaundice. When I look at pictures from that summer, my eyes are drawn to my grandpa's yellow-toned complexion. Almost a year later, he passed away.

I wish I could say that year was filled with nothing but happiness and memories to last us forever, but it wasn't. It was filled with lots of sadness. After trying treatment, my grandpa refused chemotherapy because of how bad it made him feel. Months before he died, my mom moved up to Pennsylvania to be with him. My dad took me and my siblings to visit almost every weekend; and, when my grandpa died, we missed almost a week of school. I can remember the day we found out like it was yesterday. I may not have been very old, but this experience shaped who I was and who I became. This experience led me to the path of medicine.

The sad thing is, my story is just a drop in the ocean of the stories that reflect the devastating impact of cancer. Cancer affects millions of lives. In fact, it is the second-leading cause of death in the United States [1]. Sadly, though, it disproportionately affects Kentucky. Kentucky has the highest cancer incidence and mortality rates in the United States [1, 2].

I used college as a way to educate myself on this disparity.

I applied and was generously offered a position in the Appalachian Career Training in Oncology (ACTION) Program at UK. This program gave endless possibilities to find cancer research, outreach, and opportunities to grow. I partnered with a professor here at UK to mentor me and, through her research, to learn more about cancer disparities in Kentucky. I wanted to know why cancer is so prevalent here, so I read up on barriers that keep Kentuckians from acquiring screening and, thus, failing to prevent cancer.

Sadly, this is a long list: lack of finances and insurance; low accessibility of healthcare services, screening tests, or test sites; barriers related to transportation; lack of knowledge of cancer risk and cultural determinants of health behavior; low prioritization of health; and, most interesting to me, fear [3]. This encompasses various fears, including fear of a positive result, fear of discomfort from cancer screenings, fear of the financial burden, and so on. Fear is such an intriguing thing to claim as a barrier, because how can we measure fear? I decided this was where I wanted to focus.

I used my mentor's data to research how a lack of knowledge contributes to fear and how this affects screening adherence. In short, we found a correlation between the two. Lack of screening is one of the main reasons that Kentucky is so disproportionately affected by cancer. The lack of education on screening, about other preventive tools, and about the cancer diagnosis itself has led to many people dying of preventable cancers. That's such a sad thought to me—especially when thinking back to my grandpa.

His cancer wasn't necessarily preventable, because symptoms don't arise until it's too far along, but if it was even just a little bit preventable, I would've wanted him to take those actions to prevent the pain he endured. I want that for everyone, but especially for the people of Kentucky.

The disproportionate cancer incidence and mortality in Kentucky doesn't just come down to a singular thing. Of course, lack of screening is a major issue, but Kentucky is ranked high in most cancer risk factors. For example, Kentucky is ranked second in the nation for cigarette smoking in those 18 and older, fifth in obesity prevalence, and low in HPV vaccination coverage [4]. These are factors that are not easily fixed. Sometimes these factors or mindsets are ingrained from a young age. Various people in my family smoke. It's just something I've grown up with, and I'm sure a lot of people have had the same experience. Although changing these things, along with other factors (such as sun exposure, lack of physical activity, etc.) may seem impossible, it can start by making small changes.

Kentucky has been trying to take action to increase preventive screenings and to decrease the incidence and mortality of cancer, but we still have a long way to go. I think the first step would be to increase educational outreach programs that would help in increasing knowledge surrounding cancer. As the saying goes, knowledge is power. These education programs could shed light on the disparities that Kentuckians face and also discuss the preventive actions that people can take. Hopefully, this would alleviate some of the many fears people have surrounding cancer.

I also think it would be beneficial to increase access to effective intervention programs for those who make certain life choices that increase the chances of cancer (such as smoking, poor diet, choosing not to get screened, etc.). These interventions can be widely successful if they are tailored to the people in the communities being targeted. Not only would these interventions possibly help lower cancer incidence, they also would help people make different choices and take charge of their health. Increasing access to testing and testing centers would also be beneficial to Kentucky. This is probably one of the hardest things to accomplish because of the resources needed to provide testing centers. Overall, though, we need to make a change.

After my grandpa died, cancer wasn't something I wanted to hear or talk about; however, as I got older, I wanted to understand it. Thankfully, the ACTION Program allowed me to do just that and more. I have grown in my understanding and in my passion to help relieve the cancer burden in Kentucky—and even more so in Eastern Kentucky. I've learned so much about what holds Kentuckians back from taking preventive action and about how we can work to remedy that. I hope to carry the knowledge I've gained about cancer research and outreach to my future career as a physician. Whether it is in rural Eastern Kentucky where I grew up or in urban Lexington where I live now, it takes students like us to influence and to drive change. It takes our determination and our compassion for the people of Kentucky to come together, support each other, educate each other, and drive each other to be better.

REFERENCES

1. R. L. Siegel et al., "Cancer Statistics, 2021," *CA: A Cancer Journal for Clinicians* 71, no. 1 (January–February 2021): 7–33, https://acsjournals.onlinelibrary.wiley.com/doi/10.3322/caac.21654.

2. "Cancer Statistics at a Glance," Centers for Disease Control and Prevention, 2021, https://www.cdc.gov/nchs/pressroom/sosmap/cancer_mortality/cancer.htm.

3. R. J. Womeodu and J. E. Bailey, "Barriers to Cancer Screening," *Medical Clinics of North America* 80, no. 1 (1996): 115–133, https://www.sciencedirect.com/science/article/pii/S0025712505704302?via%3Dihub.

4. "Cancer Statistics Center: Kentucky at a Glance," American Cancer Society, accessed 2021, https://cancerstatisticscenter.cancer.org/#!/state/Kentucky.

KENTUCKIANS FIGHT TO KEEP THEIR SIMPLE LIFESTYLE

Jessica Lamb

Appalachian Kentucky is truly a beautiful place, one that I happily call home. It is a peaceful place with flowing rivers, rolling hills, and bluegrass fields. The residents of Kentucky are connected by an appreciation for the special contributions that their home offers, such as the beautiful scenery, humble lifestyle, and creative music. Despite the many wonderful things about Kentucky, the beloved state is undergoing a healthcare crisis. Kentucky has the highest cancer incidence and mortality rates in the United States, with even higher rates in the state's Appalachian region [1].

I am an undergraduate student at the University of Kentucky, majoring in agricultural and medical biotechnology. I am on the pre-medical track, pursuing a career as a pediatric neurologist. I am from Paint Lick, Kentucky, a small farming town in Garrard County. I grew up playing in lush hayfields, blistering-hot tobacco patches, horse pastures, and dusty barns. The only public facilities in Paint Lick were a bank and a post office—until this past year when a Dollar General store was opened. Although our community is quite isolated, we love our home. The neighboring farms and families in Paint Lick have a way of seemingly becoming a single family because we share the same lifestyle. Similarly, all of the neighboring communities in Garrard County have a way of becoming one big community. Everyone smiles and waves as they pass on the road. As a child, I would play a game with my father where I challenged him to identify the people we passed on the road. I would also often challenge him to identify who lived or owned the farms that we passed on our way home from running errands. I remember always being amazed at how many people he knew so closely. As I have aged and ventured into different parts of the world, I have developed an even stronger appreciation for the small-town community and life that exists in Garrard County.

On the farm, the days seem to flow together. Everybody wakes at daylight, does their chores, and then works until sundown. Then families gather together for dinner, say their prayers, and rest for the next day of work. Work on the farm is never dreaded or despised. Those who work the farm grow to love their land and do whatever is necessary to make it and their family more prosperous. It's a simple life, one that is shared throughout Garrard County. However, this simple life meets an abrupt turn when a tragedy hits the community.

Garrard County's simple life became terribly complicated in July 2019, when one of my high school classmates, Sawyer Cornett, noticed a growing pain in his leg. Sawyer is a very bright and kindhearted young man that is well known throughout the community. Anybody you ask would have something beautiful to say about Sawyer. He was involved in many activities throughout high school, including the bowling team, engineering club, and Fellowship of Christian Athletes. He was even voted homecoming king one year. Sawyer enjoyed many things, but his true passion was for the combat sport of fencing. He had just finished his first year of college at Cleveland State University, where he was a

Division One fencer. Sawyer was back home enjoying his summer with friends and family when he began to notice a strange soreness in his upper left thigh. He initially thought nothing of the pain, as he was used to athletic aches. However, the pain continued to intensify. Sawyer began to think that he might have torn a muscle in his thigh, so his family took him to the hospital. He received an MRI and was told that it was merely cellulitis, and he was sent home with antibiotics.

However, the antibiotics did not ease the pain. In the following days, the pain was so excruciating that he couldn't walk or even bear weight on his leg. Sawyer then went to Ephraim McDowell Hospital in Danville, where he received his true diagnosis. What he had thought was a simple athletic injury had turned into something that would change his life forever. The doctors did blood work and found that Sawyer had a significantly high white blood cell count. He was diagnosed with T-cell acute lymphoblastic leukemia. Sawyer had just started his college career; he was a successful athlete, and his whole life was going his way . . . until this single moment. He would now have to begin the biggest duel of his life, only this time without his foil sword.

After receiving his diagnosis, Sawyer went to the University of Kentucky's hospital, where he spent two weeks. Sawyer received so much fluid that he gained nearly 30 pounds in water weight, which he then lost in about three days. His body was completely turmoiled. He then began receiving chemotherapy. The doctors had managed to relieve the pain in his leg for a few months, but it unfortunately returned. Sawyer went back to the hospital to learn that he had developed an infection in his leg so deep that it was nearly to the bone. He had a surgery done to remove the majority of the infection, and then a surgical drain was implanted in his leg. Sawyer described this to be his lowest point. He had to allow the remaining infection to drain for about three weeks, cleaning and "flossing" it himself three times a day. After the drain was taken out, he was left with an uncomfortably large hole in his leg.

Sawyer had to undergo more chemotherapy than he cared to remember and multiple lumbar punctures to check for cancer in his spine. The cancer didn't go away as quickly as the doctors had expected, so he had to receive radiation therapy. Radiation took the largest toll on his body, as he lost all of his hair. He lost essentially all of his muscle mass, especially in his arms and legs. He was no longer able to participate in the sport that he had loved so dearly. He was bedridden for weeks and is still isolated at home, restricted from returning to college for his sophomore year of classes and seeing his friends.

Sawyer is still fighting leukemia. He is currently in the maintenance phase of chemotherapy. This requires him to receive treatment once a month for two years, with occasional weeklong treatments. He also has a quite strenuous pill regimen that he has to follow every morning and night, which includes chemo pills. Despite all of his hardships, Sawyer continues to truly be a light and inspiration to the community. His strength, optimism, and faith have proved to be an inspiration to so many people, including myself.

Sawyer says that his primary comfort and coping mechanism continues to be his religion and faith. He realizes that at the end of the day, everything is in God's hands. He continuously tells people that it could always be worse, and he tries to take things day by day. Even with his own health conditions, Sawyer is compassionate and caring for others. He empathizes with those that have worse conditions than his own. Sawyer is still fighting strong; he was a successful swordsman, after all. He plans to return to college, continue his education, and pursue a career as a physical therapist. Sawyer says that he tries to have an open mind about everything that he experiences, as he has developed a new appreciation for life.

In Garrard County, and even in neighboring counties, cancer has seemingly become an inevitable occurrence in daily life. Everybody is affected by the disease, either directly or indirectly. Because cancer is so common, it has become easy to dismiss the seriousness of the disease and the havoc it wreaks. I have often heard people make the comment, "Well, everybody gets cancer these days. What's the point?" However, our community was forced to face cancer head-on when Sawyer was diagnosed.

Southern Roots Boutique, a local and family-owned clothing shop, made and sold T-shirts with the phrase "Sawyer Strong," and they donated all of the proceeds to Sawyer's family to help with the financial aspect of his treatment. The *Garrard Central Record* interviewed Sawyer and published a news article following his story. One of Sawyer's family friends started a GoFundMe fundraiser to support his fight against cancer, which has now raised over $15,000. It is safe to say that the entire county was touched by Sawyer's story and came together to support his fight.

When it comes down to a person sitting with their doctor and being told that they have a disease for which there is not a cure, neither the name of the disease nor the statistics behind that disease matter. Cancer is singlehandedly the disease that is most responsible for putting people in this unthinkable situation. Therefore, it is so important not to get caught up in the statistics of cancer and not to think of it as an inevitable occurrence. Instead, we must realize that behind each statistic there is an innocent human life. We must begin to think of the fight against cancer as more than just a relentless task; we should rather consider it a fight for humanity, a fight for *life*.

This ideology is especially important to have in Kentucky. Kentucky has the highest rates in both cancer incidence and mortality. Appalachian Kentucky has a cancer mortality rate that is 36 percent higher than that of the rest of the country [1]. The top three cancers responsible for death in Kentucky include lung and bronchus, female breast, and prostate [2]. I think that cancer is so prevalent in Appalachian Kentucky due to the following reasons: unhealthy lifestyle factors, lack of access to healthcare, and lack of knowledge about the disease.

Kentucky has a significantly low level of cancer and healthcare knowledge, which is especially prominent in the Appalachian region. This dilemma plays a large role in the state's overall health trends, including cancer rates. It has been proven that people with insufficient health literacy are less likely to take preventive actions and participate in healthy lifestyle habits [3].

Unhealthy lifestyle habits such as smoking, lack of physical activity, and an unhealthy diet increase the risk of cancer. Residents of Appalachian Kentucky report a smoking rate that is 1.8 times higher than in other places of the nation. Obesity rates in Kentucky are significantly higher than the rest of the United States, and the obesity rates in Appalachian Kentucky are much higher than the rest of the state [4].

Access to healthcare is very limited in Appalachian communities. Garrard County, in particular, only has a few local clinics and a health department. Residents are forced to drive long distances to visit a doctor and get proper healthcare, which oftentimes makes people not want to go until it is absolutely necessary. This proves to be extremely detrimental. One of the main reasons cancer mortality rates are so elevated in Kentucky is that most cases are not detected early enough to adequately treat the disease [5].

There are many ways to address the cancer crisis in Kentucky. Outreach and education must be a priority in order to raise awareness about the disease, its risk factors, and prevention methods. Holding cancer presentations and health fairs for middle and high schools could help educate students about the importance of routine checkups and screenings. Grade schools are the ideal audience, because students will go home and educate their families. In response to the smoking and obesity rates in the state, it may be possible to increase taxes on tobacco products and unhealthy foods. Outreach also plays a key role in this aspect of addressing the cancer crisis. Tobacco has become a widely accepted part of life in Appalachian regions of Kentucky. Garrard County has an annual Tobacco Cutting Festival to celebrate the crop. It's a tricky thing to talk about because so many farmers rely on their tobacco crops for their livelihood. However, I believe that if communities were more aware of how much tobacco contributes to the cancer crisis, they would be more open to discussing the health effects of using tobacco products. In response to limited healthcare access, pop-up clinics could open in Appalachian communities to offer affordable, or even free, screenings. Telehealth appointments could also be a possible method of treating people in secluded areas. Patients could participate in a phone call with their doctor and discuss their symptoms to see if a long drive to a hospital is necessary.

This is a fight that merits attention from doctors, educators, students, researchers, and above all, civilians. This is our fight. We must remind ourselves and our communities that although cancer may be common in our areas, it should never be casual. We must keep up with stories like Sawyer's, so that we can constantly be reminded that behind the statistics, numbers, and rates, cancer is affecting the lives of the people we love. We must keep ourselves motivated to fight for each other so we can all continue to live the simple life that we love so dearly.

REFERENCES

1. S. D. Rodriguez et al., "A Social-Ecological Review of Cancer Disparities in Kentucky," *Southern Medical Journal* 111, no. 4 (April 2018): 213–219, https://www.ncbi.nlm.nih.gov/pmc/articles/PMC5935122/.

2. "USCS Data Visualizations," Centers for Disease Control and Prevention, 2020, https://gis.cdc.gov/Cancer/USCS/DataViz.html.

3. R. A. Simmons et al., "Health Literacy: Cancer Prevention Strategies for Early Adults," *American Journal of Preventive Medicine* 53, no. 3, s. 1 (2017): S73–S77, https://www.sciencedirect.com/science/article/pii/S0749379717302064?via%3Dihub.

4. N. E. Schoenberg et al., "Trends in Cigarette Smoking and Obesity in Appalachian Kentucky," *Southern Medical Journal* 108, no. 3 (2015): 170–177.

5. "State of Lung Cancer 2020," American Lung Association, 2021, https://www.lung.org/research/state-of-lung-cancer/states/kentucky.

APPALACHIA'S PLIGHT

Tyce Riddle

In my opinion, Eastern Kentucky is one of the most beautiful places on Earth. Everything from the warm colors of the mountains in the fall to the secluded and cozy hollows simply takes my breath away. Yet, within this land of splendor, a dark and terrible disease plagues the people who call these mountains home. This disease is cancer, and it has worked its way into the very culture of Appalachia.

If you live, or have lived, in Eastern Kentucky, then odds are that either you or someone you know has had a battle with cancer. As reported by the Centers for Disease Control and Prevention (CDC), Appalachia has a higher incidence rate of cancer than anywhere else in the country [1]. It is a sad fact to be sure, but to most people it's just one common characteristic of the region. No one in Appalachia can seem to escape this plight, and I am no exception.

My name is Tyce Riddle, and I grew up in Pikeville, Kentucky. Growing up, I took a lot for granted about my hometown. I always thought that my hometown was too slow, boring, ordinary for my tastes, but I did not realize that these mundane memories would actually become some of the most precious to me. Whether it was the crisp fall air under stadium lights on a Friday night, the entire family gathered around a large table for Thanksgiving meals, or simply the vast array of reds, yellows, and oranges of the fall, each and every one of these memories holds a special place in my heart. It's exactly these memories that keep me deeply attached to my hometown even though I am no longer there. Currently I am at the University of Kentucky in Lexington, Kentucky, studying to become a physician. It was the combination of my desires to become a physician and to help my home community that led me to join the Appalachian Career Training in Oncology (ACTION) Program. The ACTION Program seemed to be the best way to finally be able to do something about this disease that has been a part of my life since childhood.

My first real experience with cancer came during middle school. This time of life is when young people finally start to realize the severity of the things that are going on in the world. During middle school there was always one teacher that everyone both simultaneously loved and feared for her caring-yet-stern attitude. So it came as a huge shock to us all when she admitted to the class one day that she had recently been diagnosed with breast cancer. Everyone in the class realized that this was something serious, but the stark reality of this situation didn't sink in until much later. After about a month into our teacher's chemotherapy treatment, she was grading papers and running her hands through her hair when a clump of her hair came loose. She didn't say anything about it, she simply got up and told us to excuse her for a moment as she walked out of the room. Just seeing the expression on her face as she realized what had happened broke my heart in that moment, and it's a feeling that I know I will never forget. However, as time went on, she continued her treatment and finally went into remission. This was the first instance in my life that I can truly recall realizing how awful of a disease cancer truly was.

It took someone that I considered to be fearless and it completely broke them down. This would not be the last time I would feel this sensation when facing cancer.

The most prominent run-in that I have ever had with cancer came during my second year of college. It was getting close to finals week when I got a random call from my older brother. He talked to me on the phone and told me that our mother had been diagnosed with stage four colorectal cancer nearly a month prior. My brother had to be the one to call me because my mom couldn't handle having that conversation with me. I remember feeling a lot of anguish and anger over the fact that they had waited for so long to tell me. Then, once it set in, I just felt completely numb. Here was another person in my life that I had always thought was untouchable, and she was about to undergo one of the toughest trials on the face of this planet.

Not long after I got this call, I had to watch my mother undergo multiple surgeries, rounds of chemotherapy, sick days, and emotional trials. And all the while, I felt completely and utterly powerless. This is the underlying tribulation within the disease cancer. Cancer not only ravages the bodies of those afflicted, it also wears on the minds and emotions of anyone that is involved. My mother has been on treatments for her cancer for well over a year now, and she has only continued to improve with her treatments. Yet we all know that nothing will be the same as it was before when this is all said and done.

These were just two stories that show how cancer has affected me personally, but stories like these are commonplace in Appalachia. Everyone has a similar story of a friend, relative, or loved one battling this atrocious disease. This disease has gripped my beautiful home with outstanding sadness and heartbreak. Yet, while no one wants this to continue on into the future, there seem to be no signs of this plight ending anytime soon. That is because in a region where cancer is deeply rooted in the culture, a lack of information—and that very culture itself—allows this disease to persist.

The Appalachian region has a very deep and rich culture. It's the home of bluegrass music and any kind of comfort food that you could want. However, there are sides to this culture that do nothing but perpetuate the high cancer rates within the region, the first part of this culture being the rampant tobacco use within Appalachia. So, just as much as everyone knows someone who has had a battle with cancer, they also know someone who uses some form of tobacco product. Growing up, I remember seeing kids start to use chewing tobacco as young as seventh grade in middle school. They'd always say something along the lines of "Well, my parents and grandparents use it, so why shouldn't I?" and most of the time, when confronted with their choices, a typical response was "So what if I get mouth cancer?" These two statements highlight one of the main reasons that I think cancer is so prevalent in Appalachia.

According to the CDC, tobacco use is the leading preventable cause of cancer and cancer deaths in our country [2]. Many of these children start using tobacco at a young age in an attempt to mirror their role models, not fully understanding the severity of their actions. Then before they know it, they're addicted. So they only serve to bolster their chances of developing cancer by using tobacco products from an early age and continue to do so throughout their lives.

While tobacco is the major leading cause of cancer development in the Appalachian region, it is not the only cause. I mentioned before that a positive aspect of the culture is the outstanding comfort food that many people take pride in. However, the truth behind this aspect of our culture is that it is a double-edged sword. In Appalachia, where most people fall into the low-socioeconomic-status category, limited choices in food and an emphasis on comfort food have greatly increased our obesity levels. According to the CDC, southeastern Appalachia has some of the highest obesity rates in the nation [3]. Furthermore, as stated by the National Cancer Institute, higher amounts of body fat have a positive correlation with the development of several types of cancer [4].

When one is placed in an environment in which they have to make a choice between a bag of cheap, processed and frozen food or a most costly, healthy bag in order to feed their family, many people would choose the option that allows them to get more for less. Or, if they do make the healthier food option, it is usually used as an ingredient in some southern comfort food, which can be just as unhealthy as the processed foods. This reality is an ordinary one for many people in Appalachia. Either they are making choices on food based off of necessity or because they want to make the homemade foods that they themselves have eaten since childhood. Whatever the reason, both options work to increase the obesity and cancer rates within the region without many people realizing this is even a problem at all.

While people generally have little control over their choices due to socioeconomic status, there is a common trend that underlies all of the problems that I have mentioned above. The underlying dilemma is a lack of information about cancer within the region itself. Everyone in the region knows that cancer is bad, but the extent of their knowledge generally ends there. I was also in this very same position before coming to college and actually learning about the disease itself. How can it be that one of the cancer capitals in our nation actually has such little understanding about the disease itself? That is why I believe getting more information to people at an early age would be one of the best ways to decrease the rates of cancer within the region.

The best way to combat a lack of information is to give people the information that they are lacking. Growing up, the only thing I ever remember learning about cancer was from a weeklong discussion about disease in my high school biology class. Even within this time period, all we learned was that cancer is a disease in which cells continue to grow, divide, and destroy other cells without stopping. Once we had this simple definition, we moved on to other topics. This should not be the only small bit of information that people learn about cancer in a place that is plagued by the disease. That is why I believe that we need to educate people from a young age in order to truly start combating this disease. By educating children as young as middle school, when children can actively begin to understand this material, we can start to influence people's decisions in a way that could mitigate the increasing cancer rates in the region.

This education should take the form of demonstrating how cancer actively grows and spreads from one area of the body to another over time; what cancer actually does to your body that leads to sickness, disease, and even death; showing how risk factors such as tobacco use and obesity actively lead to the development of cancer; and finally, by showing how cancer can be prevented and treated. To that effect, the ACTION Program is already doing an amazing job. The program is already going to high schools and middle schools and giving lectures and handing out information to young people in hopes of educating them early. However, I believe that it will take more than this to make a difference. A lecture once or twice a year will give good results, but not nearly enough that is needed to fight this plague. Schools in the Appalachian region need to make cancer a worthwhile topic in their science classes at every level, not just a one-off definition once young adults reach high school.

As I mentioned before, we should start educating people as

early as middle school about this terrible disease. At the entry level, it should be the complete basic concepts about what cancer actually is. Then every subsequent year in a science class that the students take, as they grow and mature, the lessons about cancer can start to become more complex and go more in-depth about the disease using the topics I mentioned above. If this type of integrated lesson structure was adopted by the Appalachian region, I believe the void of knowledge about this horrible disease would finally be able to be filled. By teaching people early in life and by constantly reinforcing this message, we can finally start to combat this major disease within the culture of Appalachia.

Appalachia is a beautiful place that is home to a dark and deadly disease. This region holds a special place in my heart, and I know it is worth saving. The people in this region are as strong and resilient as any group in the world, but everyone has their limits. That is why I hope the stories and insights into cancer that I have just given can be used to educate people on what cancer truly is. But more importantly, I just hope that these stories can help save my home.

REFERENCES

1. R. J. Wilson et al., "Cancer Incidence in Appalachia, 2004–2011," *Cancer Epidemiology, Biomarkers & Prevention* 25, no. 2 (2016): 250–258, https://cebp.aacrjournals.org/content/25/2/250.

2. "Cancers Linked to Tobacco Use Make Up 40 Percent of All Cancers Diagnosed in the United States," Centers for Disease Control and Prevention, accessed 2016, https://www.cdc.gov/media/releases/2016/p1110-vital-signs-cancer-tobacco.html.

3. "Highest Rates of Obesity, Diabetes in the South, Appalachia, and

Some Tribal Lands," Centers for Disease Control and Prevention, 2009, https://www.cdc.gov/media/pressrel/2009/r091119c.htm.

4. "Obesity and Cancer," National Cancer Institute, 2021, https://www.cancer.gov/about-cancer/causes-prevention/risk/obesity/obesity-fact-sheet.

A FAMILY'S PERSEVERANCE AND TOBACCO CULTURE IN APPALACHIA

Thomas Sanders

I consider myself one of the lucky ones, having been fortunate enough to have both of my parents together in our home while growing up. My mother and father did their best to raise their three children. They made great efforts to stay involved in our after-school activities as well as making sure we remained vigilant in our academic endeavors. They were both role models to me and my siblings, and they still to this day remain an integral part of all our lives.

My father has always been a man of few words. When he does speak, his ability to silence a room can be deafening. His words carry such strength that all in his presence revere his wisdom. He is a role model to several young men, as he served for many years as a scoutmaster in a Boy Scout troop. He had also been a high school teacher for many years, passing along his knowledge and love for science to the many generations of young adults who were lucky enough to have him in class. As a man of faith, my father also remained an active member of our church and passed along this strong reverence to his children. He is also my role model—someone who I could rely on to offer wisdom when I was in desperate need of direction. He inspires me to help others and give back to my community, and he is a teacher whose advice often leads to better choices in life.

My father grew up in the late '40s and early '50s, a time when tobacco regulations had not yet been introduced, and tobacco companies were actually able to advertise the idea that cigarettes were good for you. Countless advertisements featuring doctors or physicians recommending certain tobacco products can still be found online today. Throughout my youth my father would tell me stories about how he was able to purchase cigarettes for his mother at the age of six. He always liked to remind me that this was also the same age at which he tried his first cigarette. He informed me that this was a vice he wishes that he could take back, in the hopes that I would steer clear of such ill-mannered habits. From that point forward my father would become strongly addicted to cigarettes, causing unseen harm and damage to his body in the decades to come. Once my brother and I were born, he finally made the difficult decision to quit smoking. However, by that point the effects of his nicotine addiction had already caused severe damage to his body, though these effects would go unnoticed for several more years.

During my senior year of high school in the fall of 2006, I was looking forward to independence and the opportunities which awaited me at college. However, this also happened to be the time when my father would be diagnosed with cancer. I can remember the immediate emotional effects this had on our family and how each of us reacted. At the time, I can recall how extremely jarring this was for all of us to cope with and how we had been preparing for the worst. My mother immediately began doing research on how to beat the cancer and learning from the doctors the many treatments in which he would soon take part. She did her best to stay strong for her family, as my brother, my sister, and I would need all the guidance that would be necessary to keep us together. I dealt with this news a bit differently though. Although I attempted to stay positive, just like my father had taught me to be, I struggled with the unbearable, harsh reality that I could lose him.

I entered my freshman year of college as I continued to cope with our family's new reality and quickly began to lose my way. I soon bounced around many social gatherings, searching for answers and finding it difficult to manage the emotional burden of it all. My mother continued to take my father to all his medical visits in the coming year, as she was able to manage his engagements as well as his emotional stability. She possesses an uncanny ability to remain strong during difficult times and was even able to keep my father motivated throughout his initial treatments. Due to her diligence with regards to my father's appointments, along with the love and support from my siblings and myself, we were able to successfully get my father the treatment he so desperately needed. Since that time, he has needed to receive several yearly treatments and checkups, as he regularly needs to have the cancer removed from his body. He continues to go in and out of remission but finds reasons to remain positive because that is his personality, and that is who he raised me to be. After he received his cancer diagnosis in 2006, he has since been diagnosed with chronic obstructive pulmonary disease (COPD), atrial fibrillation, and now, more recently, Parkinson's disease.

My family has spent long days taking turns driving my father to and from the hospital, countless hours in waiting rooms, but we would not hesitate to do it over again. Even among all the chronic ailments that plague my father, I can truly say that my family has been so blessed that God has allowed him to stay with us for as long as he has. Other families are not always as fortunate. The use of cigarettes has had a profound effect on my father's life, and for the last 14 years I have witnessed the deterioration of his body. The daily use of tobacco has caused him to now lead a very sedentary lifestyle, as he relies heavily on my mother and my siblings for care. He has difficulty breathing daily and struggles immensely even with the most basic, rudimentary tasks. It is a heartbreaking and gut-wrenching sight to see a once proud and strong man struggle with the tasks of everyday life. Even so, he continues to inspire me by staying strong for his family, and I commend him for maintaining such a positive outlook. I hold no ill will or blame for his use of tobacco; I am extremely proud to be his son. It is no fault of my father's, for he grew up in a time when nobody knew the detrimental effects of tobacco, while our country was being told that cigarettes were good for your health.

Today, however, we live in a completely different world, but our youth continue to be baited by big tobacco companies and sold products in a much more creative fashion compared to the past. There are now many more flavors to choose from among smoking or vaping products particularly, including popular flavors such as cotton candy or bubble gum. These products are targeted at a specific audience for a very specific purpose: to get our youth addicted at an early age with the intention of selling as much product as possible. I come from a family known for their harsh realities of addiction and admittedly have learned the difficult lesson myself that once you allow tobacco to creep into your life it is incredibly difficult to eradicate it.

Every day across America, our youth are being subjugated by big tobacco companies. Throughout the Appalachian states, like Kentucky and North Carolina, tobacco remains deeply integrated into the culture and continues to be a vital economic crop throughout the region. Several families still rely on the production and distribution of tobacco to sustain their livelihood, and the crop can be seen in the many hundreds of thousands of fields all over rural areas across the state. It is difficult to imagine life in Appalachia without seeing tobacco fields throughout these areas. However, there are many pragmatic ways in which we may be able to suppress some of the sales to our youth and, over time, decrease the amount of sales that the tobacco companies produce overall.

In 2019, the US passed legislation called Tobacco 21, which bars the sale of tobacco products to those under the age of 21. It will be interesting to discover and research the gradual effects that this legislation will have on our youth. For example, since the legal age has been raised from 18 to 21, the prevalence of tobacco products in high schools and middle schools will surely experience a decline. Some other ways in which we might be able to decrease the prevalence of tobacco use, particularly across the Appalachian region, would be the inclusion of cancer education and tobacco awareness within the rural areas. It would be wise for our political leaders to pass such legislation requiring specific health courses devoted to tobacco use in schools, as we have done in the past with sexual health education. This may discourage the use of tobacco and hopefully lead to an overall increase of health promotion. Health officials, local hospitals, and community health centers in more rural areas of the state should be responsible for taking a more direct approach to deliver health education to the community and provide other opportunities to increase the level of health literacy of its members in these areas. Incremental changes such as these may help spread cancer awareness amongst teenage users and those without access to healthcare.

Aside from reforms within the healthcare community, tobacco companies should be held responsible for the negative influences that impact our youth. As mentioned before, these companies manufacture specific flavors for a specific purpose, and that is because those flavors are being most consumed by a younger audience. I would like to see tobacco companies barred from selling such flavors, restricted only to the sale of the more traditional flavors like natural or straight. Also, the removal of the harsh chemical compounds found in many tobacco products may go a long way towards lessening the devastating effects of the product to those who are currently addicted.

As we move forward in our small communities across Kentucky, it is most important that we strive to spread tobacco awareness across the region, especially among those in rural Appalachia. All too often, lives are taken too early from families, wives, husbands, daughters, and sons. Still, to this day, people across the Appalachian region of Kentucky continue to use tobacco at an alarming rate, and its inhabitants are not being informed properly about how tobacco can affect their lives. Less-addictive and chemically potent tobacco products would be a major improvement of the products being sold to those who are in dire need of a substitute to alleviate the detrimental effects of tobacco. It is important that we remain vigilant in our pursuit of spreading health education and tobacco awareness across this great state, providing health literacy programs to those in need of support in our rural communities. We must also remain steadfast to our commitment of applying pressure to big tobacco companies, ensuring dramatic changes take place with regard to their advertising markets and alteration of their products.

CANCER'S IMPACT ON KENTUCKY

Savannah Saylor

I am from Madison County, Kentucky, a community that is more closely associated with its proximity to Lexington, the heart of the Bluegrass, than it is connected to the stereotypical assumptions made about the Appalachian region of our great commonwealth. While I do not live in a small, rural town in the foothills of the Appalachian Mountains, my family tree is deeply rooted in Eastern Kentucky given that my dad was born and raised in Harlan County. Because of this, much of my childhood was consumed with stories my dad told of his own childhood adventures in Harlan. I also remember countless car trips down the interstate to visit my grandparents and the endless aunts, uncles, and cousins that still live there.

One of my earliest childhood memories is hearing about when my dad's mom, my granny, was diagnosed with breast cancer in 1996, five years before I was born. She received numerous treatments and had multiple surgeries to remove the cancerous tissues from her body. She recovered well initially and was cancer free for almost ten years, but she took a turn for the worse in February of 2005 when she was diagnosed with a form of uterine cancer. This cancer was much more aggressive and spread quickly, reaching her brain.

Although I was only three years old at the time of her second diagnosis, I can remember visiting my granny in the hospital before her first brain surgery. My granny was one of the toughest and most caring women I knew. Obviously, at three years old, I struggled to understand what the scary word "cancer" really meant, but I knew that my granny was in pain and my entire family was struggling because of it. On the day of her brain surgery, with the entire family gathered around, I sat at the foot of her hospital bed and sang her a song that I had memorized at Sunday school. I only remember bits and pieces of that day, but a couple of things that stood out to me were the sound of my parents crying and the bittersweet feeling of hugging my granny before she was taken away for surgery. Not being able to grasp the complete seriousness of the situation and what that day meant regarding my granny's health, I simply understood that she was hurting and needed to know how deeply she was loved.

To this day, the song that I sang remains so important to me. I still remember every word. I am reminded of my granny's tenacity and sheer love for life every time I sing it. One of the most important verses in the song says: "Waking, sleeping, I am with you, never alone." Although I didn't realize it at the time, that song fully embodies the message I hope every individual that is diagnosed with cancer hears. Having to fight the battle against cancer with a loving support system is so much better than fighting alone. However, I recognize that this is impossible in some cases. It breaks my heart to think of all the individuals who are fighting a cancer battle with no one to love or support them. My family was blessed to be able to help my granny bear the burden of her disease and spend every day with her until her last moments. Unfortunately, she passed away in September of

2005, so all I have left of her now are memories and stories that my family members tell. Even in sickness, she was the toughest woman I knew, always putting the needs of others before her own. The greatest lesson that I learned from my granny during this experience was that, especially in the darkest moments, love is the most precious gift.

More recently, I witnessed my granny's younger sister, my Great-Aunt Gladys, fight her own battle with cancer. She also lived in Harlan, Kentucky, and did not have easy access to the healthcare and adequate cancer treatments she needed. On top of that, she simply refused to seek medical care. I recently learned that she found out about her own breast cancer diagnosis at the same time that my granny was receiving chemotherapy and radiation treatments for her initial diagnosis. However, because my great-aunt witnessed all the pain that my granny went through during her treatments, she decided that she didn't want to have anything done if it meant putting herself through the same agony. She said that she wanted to leave her health in the Lord's hands; she never had treatments of any kind. At first, there were minimal consequences to her decision. For about 15 years, she seemed as healthy as ever. I am sure she endured great discomfort and many sleepless nights, but she, like my granny, was a stubborn woman who never wanted to be a burden to others. It wasn't until about 2016 that it became obvious the cancer had taken a toll on her body. She became weak and struggled to accomplish mundane tasks, spending most of her time sitting alone in her living room. After that, her health worsened rapidly. My family visited her as often as we could, but there wasn't much that we could do to help ease her pain. During one visit, I can remember my dad asking her how she was doing. Her arm had swollen to about three times its normal size, and she removed a cotton bandage from her chest to reveal a gaping hole where her left breast had once been. It was shocking and devastating that she was enduring such pain because of her cancer. She passed away shortly after that day.

From stories I have heard about their childhood, I know that my granny and Great-Aunt Gladys were inseparable. They shared so many admirable qualities, such as their contagious smiles, stubborn love, unconditional optimism, and ever-present desire to help people. They also shared similar cancer diagnoses. Although their cancer journeys were complete opposites, their stories are similar, and the terrible disease took both of their lives. They both taught me so much about the true meaning of strength.

As a student at the University of Kentucky, I am pursuing a degree in neuroscience. I hope to one day attend medical school to become a doctor so that I can help people who have similar stories to my granny and Aunt Gladys. I know that my involvement in the Appalachian Career Training in Oncology (ACTION) Program will help enhance my understanding of the effects of cancer in Kentucky and allow me to do my part in changing the way cancer is perceived in my old Kentucky home. I hope to use my own strength, which I learned from my granny and Aunt Gladys, to fight Kentucky's cancer battle and support those who need it most.

Unfortunately, my own personal experiences with cancer are not unusual in any way in Eastern Kentucky. Cancer impacts Kentuckians, especially those that reside in the Appalachian region of our state, at a much higher rate than in any other state in the US [1, 2]. I believe that this is because of the high presence of risk factors in Kentucky and lack of information to which citizens of rural communities have access. Poverty is also a huge issue. Rural Kentuckians have relied on a subsistence lifestyle ever since Kentucky was first inhabited. This stagnant, existence-oriented way of life has stunted the improvements that need to be made economically and educationally, but most importantly in healthcare and cancer treatment. Cancer screenings need to occur more frequently, and steps need to be taken to prevent the likelihood of cancer incidence. These steps must begin with increased funding and educational services that strive to take preventive action against cancer. The best way to beat cancer is to prevent it.

One of the most important factors in addressing cancer in Kentucky is simply increasing awareness. Educating communities, especially those in rural areas where cancer screenings are few and far between, can help people improve their understanding of what cancer truly is, the factors that contribute to cancer development, and why the disease will continue to have such harsh implications if lifestyle changes do not occur. The ACTION Program focuses on educating communities about cancer through outreach initiatives and training students like myself for future careers in oncology. The work that the ACTION Program has accomplished in the past few years is so vital to the progress made in Kentucky's fight against the cancer epidemic. But we can't stop there. Raising awareness isn't enough to combat the high rate of cancer incidence in Kentucky. The next step is to take action, and action begins with the individual. It is up to each and every Kentuckian, both in Appalachia and otherwise, to take precautionary measures and devote time and resources to reducing the devastating effects of cancer on innocent people. I hope to one day live in a world where there is a cure and cancer is no longer a fear. Sadly, I know that day has yet to come. Until then, it is all we can do to help our fellow Kentuckians by actively devoting ourselves to cancer education and preventing exposure to the associated risk factors. Actively supporting the communities in which cancer is an increased risk is just one way to support this important cause. The easiest way is to simply show compassion. Reach out to your neighbors. Be the support system that they need as they fight this unimaginable battle, and never forget how easy it is to share your own strength and contagious love.

Cancer's obvious prevalence in Appalachia is a devastating statistic that impacts every Kentuckian. While we strive to improve cancer detection, treatment, and healthcare availability for the future, it is just as important right now for everyone to develop healthier lifestyle habits so my granny and great-aunt's cancer stories are no longer the norm in Kentucky.

REFERENCES

1. "USCS Data Visualizations," Centers for Disease Control and Prevention, 2020, https://gis.cdc.gov/Cancer/USCS/DataViz.html.

2. S. D. Rodriguez et al., "A Social-Ecological Review of Cancer Disparities in Kentucky," *Southern Medical Journal* 111, no. 4 (April 2018): 213–219, https://www.ncbi.nlm.nih.gov/pmc/articles/PMC5935122/.

KENTUCKY'S RACE AGAINST CANCER

Alexia ShamaeiZadeh

As I drive down the interstate of the Mountain Parkway, I am surrounded by the beautiful Appalachian Mountains. I am comforted by the serenity of the landscape, and I suddenly acquire this wholesome feeling of peace. However, the beauty and serendipity of this landscape belies the disparities of the rural area. The countryside does not show the effect cancer has had on the place I call home. Fortunately, not everyone can say that they live in the cancer capital of America. Kentucky is distinctly known to have the leading incidence and mortality rates of cancer per capita in the United States [1-3], and it is known that the eastern region of Kentucky faces significantly higher rates of cancer mortality and morbidity [2, 4].

My name is Alexia ShamaeiZadeh, and I am originally from Paintsville, Kentucky. As I grew up in the heart of Eastern Kentucky, I knew the social stigma: My community was viewed as uneducated individuals who lived in a town with one stoplight. When I met people from outside of my region or state, they would commonly ask if we wore shoes or had adequate drinking water.

However, I credit my hometown with the quality education that sparked my interest in national cancer rates. Paintsville High School pointed me in the direction of the dream to become a physician—someone who held an arsenal of knowledge and firmly believed in bettering the lives of others.

When I came to the University of Kentucky to pursue my dream of becoming a physician, I had no idea that the journey would be as eye-opening or rewarding as it has been thus far. It was not until I joined the Appalachian Career Training in Oncology (ACTION) Program that I gained so much knowledge within the field of oncology.

As a native Kentuckian, I find it nearly impossible to ignore the fact that cancer rates are higher in Kentucky than in other states in the country. Reflecting on what it was like to live in Eastern Kentucky before moving to Lexington, I realize how many factors influence the high cancer rates that exist in this state, especially my home region. Cancer, which occurs when cells overproduce in abnormal ways and compete for the space that normal cells occupy, is a growing problem for us to solve. Currently, cancer is the second leading cause of death in Americans, and the cost of cancer care is expected to reach almost $174 billion by 2020 [1, 3]. Research is underway to identify new treatments and preventive methods for this chronic disease.

With the ACTION Program, I am grateful to have worked in a research lab which requires me to read scholarly articles to learn the latest research methods. There are many risk factors associated with developing cancer, and researchers are constantly working on innovative screenings to detect cancer early. It is important that research be conducted to understand the complex mechanisms that cause cancer as well as to learn what can be done to prevent it and to reduce its comorbidities. Reading how complicated it is to simply "solve cancer" allowed me to reach for a realistic goal for my community. This hands-on training in research shaped my path to combat the problem by taking a proactive approach to achieve lower cancer rates in Kentucky.

Eastern Kentucky is a remote area with lack of access to healthcare services and transportation. I never realized the true health disparity until my grandmother battled stage four liver cancer in 2007. Although I was young, it was not long until I was made aware that my extended family had to travel two hours for every appointment with the specialty physician. It is well known that there is a lack of specialty physicians in the Appalachian region; there are 59 percent fewer specialty doctors in Appalachian Kentucky compared to the nation and 60 percent fewer than in non-Appalachian Kentucky [4]. Without immediate access to specialty physicians, cancer rates will undeniably rise. The lack of access to healthcare and treatment programs exacerbates the risk factors that can propagate a disease. Unfortunately, most of the residents in Eastern Kentucky live in rural areas and do not have the access to physicians or to transportation to receive the care or treatment needed. My grandmother's liver cancer was discovered at stage four when she went for an appointment that was scheduled almost two months in advance. As her cancer worsened, we had no choice but to wait for what felt like a lifetime. This is just one story of the health disparities in Appalachia. As such, lack of access to specialty physicians is the main barrier that we must work to break.

In addition to health disparities, it has been found that obesity rates have influenced many different types of cancers, including endometrial, pancreatic, colon, and breast cancer. The correlation between underlying obesity and cancer is the reason I chose to major in human nutrition at the University of Kentucky.

There is a link to tumor cell growth due to insulin growth factors, also known as IGFs. Human nutrition is not necessarily the first thought that comes to a physician's mind when a patient is diagnosed with cancer, but it should be one of the first considerations. Obesity is an underlying health issue for many people in Eastern Kentucky. With the education I have received at the University of Kentucky, I believe that developing proper diets and reducing obesity rates will aid as a preventive measure for cancer rates in my community. The proactive approach I hope to implement in my community begins with raising awareness to prevent the prevalence of underlying health issues.

Along with obesity, scientists say tobacco habits are also on the list of preventable risk factors that can cause the negative health outcome of cancer. Smoking behavior is an extremely common habit in my hometown, yet smoking cessation programs are extremely uncommon. Substance abuse in Eastern Kentucky is incredibly frequent, even after the age restriction to purchase tobacco was raised to 21. Four out of five counties with the highest lung cancer deaths in 2014 were in Eastern Kentucky [5]. The issue, in addition to easy access to tobacco, lies with insurance coverage for lung cancer screenings. Medicaid programs are one of the only healthcare payers that are not required to cover lung cancer screenings [6].

My uncle, who resided in Louisa, Kentucky, was diagnosed with stage two lung cancer just five years after my grandmother had passed. However, while catching his lung cancer at such an early age seemed like a glimpse of hope, insurance was a barrier to care. It was difficult for my uncle to receive treatment after his diagnosis because of the high cost. Unfortunately, my uncle's lung cancer progressed at a rapid rate. If there was equal access to lung cancer screening with Medicaid insurance, I believe his battle, and other battles in Eastern Kentucky, may have been different. All of these factors intersect to create a variety of barriers for those who wish to seek preventable care or treatment for cancer.

Throughout my life, losing my grandmother and my uncle was hard-hitting; it showed me the true fragility of life like never before. I knew I wanted to turn my interests into my pursued career. Upon joining the ACTION Program, I have been presented with many opportunities to immerse myself in the knowledge that this program has shown me. Before this program, I knew very little about how I was going to achieve my dream. I knew my dream, but I was unsure of the logistics and how to actually get started on my journey toward giving back to my community. This experience has provided me with the tools I need to ultimately give back to my community. For example, this past year I was able to help ACTION pair with my high school to speak to those who are directly affected by the cancer crisis. In Eastern Kentucky, there is misinformation and inadequate education relative to cancer, and this was the first step to raising awareness of the cancer crisis in my community.

Raising awareness of the risk factors of cancer is my main focus right now. It was found by Whitney Zahnd, PhD, that cancer rates associated with risks that can be modified—tobacco, HPV, and those that can be screened for (colorectal cancer, cervical cancer, etc.)—are higher in rural populations compared to urban. Reasons behind this statistic can be attributed to higher rates of poverty, more individuals with Medicaid insurance, and more barriers to healthcare access [7].

With ACTION, I have been able to pair with members from my hometown to gather information for outreach in my community. To avoid confusion, we focus on one type of cancer at a time. For example, we set up a booth at our community fair for the HPV vaccine. Along with talking about the vaccine, it was important to target the ages for which the vaccine is recommended; it was equally important to vocalize the preventive measures of many cases of cervical cancer, vaginal cancer, anal cancer, and more.

Outreach with the help of the ACTION Program has allowed me to utilize my education for my community. I know I am already making a difference in my area, even while still learning something new every day. There are many other factors that have been discussed, but educating people on what I have learned thus far is the first step toward decreasing cancer rates in Eastern Kentucky.

The Appalachian cancer crisis is an unsettling reality. I aspire to have a career in oncology to improve equal access to healthcare and to diminish health disparities in Eastern Kentucky. I aspire to provide better access to treatment programs to slow the rate of the propagation of this disease. I aspire to advocate for proper education toward health problems that are increasing the incidence and mortality rates of cancer in our area. I aspire to prevent the factors that create barriers for those who wish to seek preventive care or treatment for cancer. I will do this for the ones with similar stories to my grandmother and uncle. I will fight health disparities for my community in hopes that we will overcome the Appalachian cancer crisis.

REFERENCES

1. "USCS Data Visualizations," Centers for Disease Control and Prevention, 2020, https://gis.cdc.gov/Cancer/USCS/DataViz.html.

2. S. D. Rodriguez et al., "A Social-Ecological Review of Cancer Disparities in Kentucky," *Southern Medical Journal* 111, no. 4 (April 2018): 213–219, https://www.ncbi.nlm.nih.gov/pmc/articles/PMC5935122/.

3. R. L. Siegel et al., "Cancer Statistics, 2021," *CA: A Cancer Journal for Clinicians* 71, no. 1 (January–February 2021): 7–33, https://acsjournals.onlinelibrary.wiley.com/doi/10.3322/caac.21654.

4. "Appalachian Health Disparities: Eastern Kentucky Has More Mental Health Providers, but Fewer of Most Other Docs than Rest of Com-

monwealth," Foundation for a Healthy Kentucky, 2017, https://www.healthy-ky.org/newsroom/news-releases/article/112/appalachian-health-disparities-eastern-kentucky-has-more-mental-health-providers-but-fewer-of-most-other-docs-than-rest-of-commonwealth.

5. T. Mandell, "Eastern Kentucky Has Some of the Nation's Highest Cancer Mortality Rates, Study Finds," Kentucky Health News, January 25, 2017, https://ci.uky.edu/kentuckyhealthnews/2017/01/25/eastern-kentucky-has-some-of-nations/.

6. "State of Lung Cancer 2020," American Lung Association, 2021, https://www.lung.org/research/state-of-lung-cancer/states/kentucky.

7. W. E. Zahnd et al., "Rural-Urban Differences in Cancer Incidence and Trends in the United States," *Cancer Epidemiology, Biomarkers & Prevention* 27, no. 11 (2018): 1265–1274.

A CHANGE ROOTED IN FAITH

Madison Tackett

Appalachia is built around family, and that includes more than just blood relation. This family is found everywhere. A trip to the local Walmart for milk can take an hour because you talk to your mother's brother's wife's second cousin. Because of this, I never went without a candy bar or water at a high school football game if I had no cash, because someone my dad graduated with would pay for me, even if I did not know them. Wherever you go here, people that know and love you are present, and they will give everything they have just to make sure their neighbor is taken care of. When I leave Lexington to travel home to Appalachia on the Mountain Parkway, I find myself praying and thanking God for my hometown every single time. I know that Appalachia is where I am meant to be. However, Appalachia, like every other place, has its own devastations. Having been born in Appalachia, I have seen and felt heartbreak caused by the ugly "C" word—cancer.

I am the granddaughter of a man who passed away at 48 years old due to colon cancer, the girlfriend of a man whose mother passed away with lung cancer when he was 15 years old, and a friend of two people that lost their fathers to cancer before they could see them graduate from high school. I have even had a terrifying appointment with an oncologist myself. This narrative is not unusual. It is not a bout of bad luck in the community; it is "normal" life in Appalachia, though it most definitely should not be considered normal.

I am from a small town in Pike County, Kentucky. When asked, I tell people I am from Pikeville, although I am actually from Virgie, a town about 16 miles south of Pikeville. There is no stoplight. We have one place to eat, a locally owned diner. Our homes are built wherever they will fit in hollers. I like to describe a holler as a one-way road, either unpaved or has not been repaved in many years, nestled between two mountains, with a creek on one side. While it may be easier to just say that I am from Pikeville, my hometown of Virgie is just that: my home.

Due to my appreciation of these mountains, I have known what career path I wanted to pursue since I was in middle school. My goal is to return home to the mountains and provide quality healthcare to the people I love. When I moved to Lexington to attend the University of Kentucky, I felt terrible for leaving the region that I care so deeply about. Where I am from, we are praised for "making it out" of the mountains, but I did not see it as something I should have been applauded for. Although I knew that it was the best option for me at the time, I felt like I was leaving my people behind. I decided that the best way for me to still help my region was to immerse myself into programs and organizations that assist in the changes we so desperately need. Currently, I hold an internship position at the American Cancer Society, participate in the Appalachian Career Training in Oncology Program, volunteer at the Hope Lodge and Ronald McDonald House, and serve as a DanceBlue team captain. This past school year, I also declared a minor in Appalachian studies. I fully intend to move back to the mountains permanently, but for now, the impact I make on my hometown through these activities keeps me satisfied.

Through my research and involvement, I found that not only does Kentucky have the highest age-adjusted rate of new cancer diagnoses, but we also have the highest age-adjusted rate of cancer deaths in the nation [1-3]. That statistic is horrifying, but I have hope that these numbers can be lowered. What is even more horrifying is that most people in my community are aware that they are more likely to develop cancer, but they feel like there is no way to change that. I believe the reason Appalachians accept this statistic is because we are called uneducated hillbillies and rednecks. Of course, I do not think this is true, but I know that hearing this every day would make anyone feel unworthy, accepting of the fact that they are more likely to hear those words. I know that, as of now, my community will not stop hearing that ugly "C" word. We will not stop hearing that diagnosis; that conversation at the doctor's office will not cease to occur. Those cards are inevitable, but that does not mean it is the end for us. The things we can change revolve around healthcare access, including insurance and transportation, which will greatly increase our chances of surviving it.

A pivotal change in our healthcare occurred when the coal industry declined. The economy in Appalachia suffered—and still does—due to the industry's breakdown. According to the Kentucky Energy and Environment Cabinet, "Employment at Kentucky coal mines decreased by 30 percent from an average of 9,557 in 2015" [4]. This downfall did more than take away job opportunities; it resulted in many Appalachians losing health insurance. Without insurance, people are very unlikely to go to the physician when they need to. They neglect routine appointments and preventive measures because it is impossible to afford. It is almost always too late by the time they go to an appointment.

On top of paying outrageous medical bills, Appalachians have a large travel barrier in receiving healthcare. My mother lives 45 minutes away from the hospital in Pikeville. If we did not have a car, we would not have the ability to get there. In my county, there is one form of public transportation, a small busing system, to take residents to appointments, preventive screenings, and pharmacies. However, it cannot provide for the whole population. The buses are too small for the large demand in our area. Of course, this transportation barrier is even more apparent for appointments farther away. Lexington, which is three hours away, is where many people from Eastern Kentucky are sent for appointments, especially for specialists. Many more financial issues come with this, including lodging, missing work, meals, and gas. These are nearly impossible to afford for most people, especially with the downfall of our economy.

The best solution to our barriers is to change our healthcare in Appalachia. If we did this, we would not need to address as many outside factors. This change starts with Appalachian healthcare providers staying in Appalachia to practice. We need people who understand the population and culture to heal the area. People from Appalachia understand the importance of the coal industry; the culture surrounding tobacco and cigarettes; the need for cheap, although unhealthy, fertilizers for gardens; and the taste of a greasy home-cooked meal made with lard. Our culture does not help our health outcomes, and it is important that patients are educated on how these habits affect their well-being. However, I have seen firsthand how patients can react if the educator does not come from a place of understanding. Don't get me wrong; it is very important to lower the smoking and tobacco rates. In fact, according to the National Cancer Institute State Cancer Profiles, Pike County, Kentucky has the highest age-adjusted incidence rate of oral cavity and pharynx cancer [5]. This is a direct result of my home county's high rates of tobacco use. However, I believe the root issue, our healthcare access, can be fixed by keeping Kentucky healthcare providers in Kentucky. We cannot expect physicians from urban areas to understand Appalachia as well as natives do, but natives are hesitant to stay. The economy fell after the coal industry plummeted. Our school system is said to be inferior to other areas. Our cost of living is nearly impossible to afford due to utility companies monopolizing the area. Electricity bills in Appalachia can end up being nearly a fourth of the resident's annual income [6]. I cannot blame Appalachians for leaving; they leave for better opportunities. I just know that our economy and healthcare system will not improve without them.

With the combination of the younger generation leaving for better opportunities and the older generation traveling to other places for medical care, the healthcare system in Appalachia will not get better. Our outcomes will not improve. The change starts with us, Appalachians. I wholeheartedly believe that, and I do not doubt for a second that we can do it with our love for each other. All it takes is one person to ignite a passion for this change by demonstrating that people can be successful in these mountains. After all, seeing this demonstrated with my own eyes is what began this passion in me.

REFERENCES

1. "State Cancer Profiles: Incidence Rate Tables," National Cancer Institute, 2021.

2. R. L. Siegel et al., "Cancer Statistics, 2021," *CA: A Cancer Journal for Clinicians* 71, no. 1 (January–February 2021): 7–33, https://acsjournals.onlinelibrary.wiley.com/doi/10.3322/caac.21654.

3. S. D. Rodriguez et al., "A Social-Ecological Review of Cancer Dis-

parities in Kentucky," *Southern Medical Journal* 111, no. 4 (April 2018): 213–219, https://www.ncbi.nlm.nih.gov/pmc/articles/PMC5935122/.

4. "Kentucky Coal Facts," Kentucky Energy and Environment Cabinet, Department for Energy Development and Independence, 2017.

5. "State Cancer Profiles," National Cancer Institute, 2020, https://statecancerprofiles.cancer.gov/recenttrend/index.php?0&4221&9599&001&999&00&1#results.

6. "KFTC Members Continue to Build New Power Through the Power House Workshops," Kentuckians for the Commonwealth, 2018, https://www.kftc.org/blog/kftc-members-continue-build-new-power-through-power-house-workshops.

MINING CANCER OUT OF KENTUCKY

Xiaomei Zheng

Out of all the 120 counties in Kentucky, each with its own unique stories and traditions, my parents opened a Chinese restaurant in the small coal-mining town of Harlan. My parents chose Harlan for a variety of reasons. Most importantly, Harlan stood out to them as a place where community was valued above all else, and they knew it was the perfect place to raise their children. My name is Xiaomei Zheng, but I go by a simple name of Lala. I am the middle child of my family of six. In this little coal-mining town, I have experienced some of my most cherished memories, but I have also witnessed some of the most devastating situations.

From an early age, I learned to be terrified of the word "cancer." Anyone with experience with the word understands that there is the pre-cancer life and then there is the post-cancer life. The post-cancer life is the part of life that is analogous to a roller coaster with its many ups and downs. I have been living in the post-cancer life due to my godmother, who was diagnosed with breast cancer when I was only six years old. My godmother has been like a grandmother to me, and her diagnosis took a huge toll on our entire family. I do not have much recollection of the details of my godmother's initial fight with cancer, which was most likely due to my parents' decision to protect my siblings and me from the horrific details of cancer.

My godmother's name is Sunny. Her name perfectly describes her bright and warm personality. As my parents were in the midst of starting a new business, Sunny quickly became the caretaker of my siblings and me. My mom always reminds me that the only person who could calm me down as a child was Sunny. When my mom had tried everything to stop my crying, all Sunny had to do was hold me and I would immediately fall asleep in her arms. Sunny and her husband moved to Knoxville, Tennessee, in 2002. The move from a small town to a big city was a blessing in disguise because she was diagnosed with breast cancer in 2006. Because she was living in a bigger city, she had better access to medical resources.

All was well with Sunny until 2018, when she had a recurrence of cancer. But this time I was 18 years old and my parents could not shield me anymore. I witnessed Sunny go through her chemotherapy treatments and it was scary. But her bright and warm personality never went away—she was always full of hope. After a year of treatments, my mom sat down with me and explained that Sunny was finally in remission, but Sunny decided to stop taking the medication that lowered the chance of another recurrence. At first, I was confused as to why Sunny would risk cancer a third time. However, I eventually understood Sunny's philosophy—she had lived 70 wonderful years and she did not want to spend the rest of her days suffering from the pain and symptoms of the medication.

Sunny's cancer journey is not the only journey that has affected me. Although the coal mines that once fueled the city of Harlan are no longer as widespread, the effects of mining are still very evident throughout the population. Over time, as miners inhale large amounts of coal dust, the lungs suffer from severe scarring which impairs the overall lung function and may lead to lung cancer [1]. This damage may lead to a deadly disease called coal workers' pneumoconiosis, also known as black lung disease. Sadly, there is no treatment that can reverse the damage; however, there are medications and breathing treatments that may slow down the progression of the disease, relieve symptoms, and improve overall quality of life [1]. But with any health condition, there are expensive medical bills that seem to pile up. The 1969 Federal Coal Mine Health and Safety Act created a federally funded compensation program for miners who are disabled by black lung; however, the miners must prove that they have the disease, which can be a very long and expensive process [2]. Many miners and their families lack the resources, money, and access to legal representation to get their compensation. Without proper care, the impact of coal mining leads to complications, and one of those complications is the path to lung cancer [3]. "Mining" cancer out of Kentucky must now be the main focus in order to protect the individuals in Appalachia.

Another major public health issue that influences the high rates of cancer in Eastern Kentucky is access to health services. This can be defined as the timely use of personal health services to achieve the best health [4]. Many individuals living in Appalachian areas have to drive two to three hours to a hospital that can meet their medical needs. This is why it was a blessing in disguise that Sunny and her husband had moved to a bigger city with a hospital where Sunny had better access to medical care. Also, the inability to pay for healthcare services is due to the barriers of high cost of care and lack of insurance coverage. In Kentucky, there are approximately 260,000 individuals who are uninsured [5]. More specifically, in Harlan, approximately 2,000 individuals are uninsured, and over half of the population has WellCare as their insurance due to their low income [5, 6].

Access to quality healthcare services is vital for preventing and managing diseases such as black lung or cancer.

Being a student at the University of Kentucky has opened a multitude of doors to allow me to help my hometown and other individuals who may be affected by cancer. I am currently a senior at the University of Kentucky working towards earning my bachelor's degree in public health and my master's degree in public health with a focus in health behavior. Although public health professionals are not the professionals typically providing direct healthcare to individuals, they contribute substantially behind the scenes. One of the main tasks that public health professionals focus on is prevention, such as screening for cancers. For example, mammograms and colonoscopies are simple ways to detect breast or colon cancer in the early stages. Another type of prevention is education, which involves educating the community on topics that are hard to understand or topics that individuals may not be familiar with. As my professors say, public health's main mission is to save lives, and my goal is to do so by becoming a physician assistant (PA).

During my sophomore year at UK, I was accepted into a program called the Markey Cancer Center (MCC) Appalachian Career Training in Oncology (ACTION) Program. This program allows high school students and college students who are from the Appalachian area to be involved in opportunities to gain experience in cancer research and outreach projects. During my time in this program, I have gained experiences that I would not be able to get anywhere else. I was able to attend MCC's annual research conference, where I met my current research advisor, Dr. Jean Edward. Dr. Edward's mentorship has taught me several skills in conducting research that will prepare me for my future career. For example, I worked closely with Dr. Edward in extensively reviewing public health literature to better understand what is known about research in this area. As a sophomore and especially as a first-generation college student, this was fairly new to me; however, Dr. Edward worked diligently and patiently with me to ensure I fully understood the research process. Working with Dr. Edward has allowed me to better understand research opportunities in the field of nursing and public health. Another experience through the ACTION Program is my human papillomavirus (HPV) vaccine outreach project. ACTION allowed me to work with Dr. Nathan Vanderford, HPV experts, and other ACTION students to create an informational HPV card that will be distributed in local doctors' offices in Harlan, Montgomery, Johnson, and Powell Counties and hopefully more counties in the future. My hope is that these cards will educate citizens of those counties and increase the immunization rate for the HPV vaccine to prevent cancers that can be caused by HPV.

The ACTION Program also led me to work as a certified nurse assistant (CNA) in the inpatient unit of the MCC at the University of Kentucky Chandler Hospital. Being a CNA in the hospital has allowed me to see, clinically, how cancer affects the lives of many individuals. I have met patients from many different backgrounds and I have been able to listen to their stories. One story in particular truly motivated me to improve the resources available to rural Kentuckians. During shift change, a patient started to get weary and was beginning to have a panic attack. The patient's family member called about that time, and I spoke with them. The family member informed me that they were almost two hours away and would not be able to come back to the hospital. This devastated the patient, which only escalated his panic attack. Cancer patients have multifaceted needs, and emotional support is one of those [7]. Sadly, this patient was not able to have his family members by his side because he had to travel so far from his home for his care. Luckily, I was able to stay with him to get him situated back into bed until the night shift CNA could comfort him.

From the beginning of my life to the present, there have been various experiences that have inspired me to become an oncology PA. My hope is to help individuals like Sunny and members in my community to find the courage to fight cancer—a word that strikes so much fear. By using educational prevention and increasing healthcare access to rural Kentuckians, I believe we can replace the terrifying thoughts that accompany a cancer diagnosis with ones of hopefulness. My plan as a future oncology PA and a public health professional is to aid in improving the lives of the hardworking individuals in Appalachia and to "mine" cancer out of Kentucky.

REFERENCES

1. "Coal Worker's Pneumoconiosis (Black Lung Disease)," American Lung Association, 2020, https://www.lung.org/lung-health-diseases/lung-disease-lookup/black-lung.

2. A. Fugate, "Appalachia's New Day: Black Lung in Eastern Kentucky," Mountain Association, 2019, https://mtassociation.org/training-ideas/black-lung/.

3. "Pneumoconiosis," Johns Hopkins Medicine, 2020.

4. "Access to Health Services," HealthyPeople.gov, 2020, https://www.healthypeople.gov/2020/topics-objectives/topic/Access-to-Health-Services.

5. "Health Report Indicator: Harlan County, Kentucky," Community Commons, 2020, https://sparkmap.org/report/?REPORT=%7B%22name%22%3A%22Standard%20Report%22%2C%22contentId%22%3A%22%23cdt-report-content%22%2C%22output%22%3A%7B%22countylist%22%3Afalse%2C%22statelist

%22%3Atrue%2C%22map%22%3Atrue%2C%22breakout%22%3A true%7D%2C%22indicator%22%3A%5B32%5D%2C%22lo cation%22%3A%7B%22key%22%3A%22county%22%2C %22type%22%3A%22county%22%2C%22show_county%22%3A true%2C%22show_state%22%3Atrue%2C%22id%22%3A%5B %2221095%22%5D%2C%22name%22%3A%5B%22Harlan%20 County%2C%20KY%22%5D%7D%7D.

6. "Department for Medicaid Services Monthly Membership Counts by County," Cabinet for Health and Family Services, 2020, https://chfs. ky.gov/agencies/dms/stats/KYDWMMCCOct2020.pdf.

7. B. A. Given, C. W. Given, and S. Kozachik, "Family Support in Advanced Cancer," *CA: A Cancer Journal for Clinicians* 51, no. 4 (2001): 213–231.

ABOUT THE EDITORS

NATHAN L. VANDERFORD

Nathan was born and raised in an Appalachian county in southern-middle Tennessee. After high school, he attended the University of Kentucky (UK) as a first-generation college student, where he earned both a bachelor of science degree in agricultural biotechnology in 1999 and a doctor of philosophy (PhD) degree in biochemistry in 2008. After his PhD, he completed a postdoctoral fellowship in molecular physiology at Vanderbilt University. He also completed a master of business administration degree at Midway University in 2013.

Nathan is now an associate professor at the UK College of Medicine in the Department of Toxicology and Cancer Biology. He also holds several administrative positions, including director of the Appalachian Career Training in Oncology Program, director of administration for the Center for Cancer and Metabolism, and assistant director for research and education for the Markey Cancer Center. In these positions, he facilitates cancer research and education initiatives across the university.

Nathan is an award-winning teacher and mentor and has a strong track record of creating impactful experiential programs for students, including creating and directing the Appalachian Career Training in Oncology (ACTION) Program. He has published in leading scientific journals including *Nature, Nature Biotechnology,* and *Science,* and his work has been covered by such media outlets as *Times Higher Education, Inside Higher Ed, US News and World Report,* and *The Atlantic.*

Nathan lives in Lexington, Kentucky, with his wife and two children. He can be reached through his website at www.nathanvanderford.com or on Twitter @nlvanderford.

CHRIS PRICHARD

Chris was raised in Frenchburg, Kentucky (Menifee County), in the heart of Kentucky's Appalachian region. He earned a bachelor of arts degree in English and secondary education in 2008 from Morehead State University. He holds a master of higher education degree from the University of Kentucky.

Chris has worked with secondary students throughout Eastern Kentucky for more than 10 years. He is currently program coordinator for the Appalachian Career Training in Oncology Program at the University of Kentucky's Markey Cancer Center.

ACKNOWLEDGMENTS

The essays in this book were written by participants in the Appalachian Career Training in Oncology (ACTION) Program, which is a Youth Enjoy Science Program funded by the National Cancer Institute under grant number R25 CA221765. Funds from the grant offset the cost of publishing this book. Additional funding was provided by the University of Kentucky (UK) Office for Institutional Diversity, the UK Chellgren Center, and the Markey Cancer Foundation. Special thanks go to Dr. Sonja Feist-Price (former vice president for institutional diversity at UK and now provost and vice chancellor at the University of Michigan–Flint), Dr. Philipp Kraemer (director of the Chellgren Center), and Michael Delzotti (president and CEO of the Markey Cancer Foundation). The book would not have been possible without support from the National Cancer Institute and these institutional partners. Thank you.

I thank Butler Books for publishing this book. I am especially grateful for Carol Butler (president and publisher of Butler Books) for her delightful character and excitement about ACTION and these essays. Thank you, Carol, for working with us to make the second edition of *The Cancer Crisis in Appalachia* come to life. Thanks also to all those at Butler Books who helped with the book.

I thank Chris Prichard, who works diligently to coordinate the ACTION Program and to keep our students on task! His organization and coordination expertise have been critical to the development of the essays. I thank Lauren Hudson for sharing her writing expertise and insights with our high school students. I also thank Joseph Harris for conducting helpful writing workshops with our high school students. Thanks also to the Markey Cancer Center's Research Communications Office, especially Donna Gilbreath and Terry Keys, for copyediting support.

Lastly, thanks to all the students who worked very hard writing their essays and for bearing with me during the rounds and rounds of my edits and comments! I thank the students for sticking with me and telling great stories. Each student did a great job and I am very proud of each and every one. Thanks also to the students' families for their trust and support. ACTION and this book would not be possible without the support of our students' families. Thank you!

—Nathan L. Vanderford, PhD, MBA
Director, Appalachian Career Training in Oncology
(ACTION) Program